THE SINGAPORE
MODEL
METHOD
for Learning Mathematics

Ministry of Education
SINGAPORE

© 2009 Curriculum Planning & Development Division
   Ministry of Education, Singapore
Illustrations © 2009 Panpac Education Private Limited

Published by EPB Pan Pacific

An imprint of Panpac Education Private Limited
Times Centre
1 New Industrial Road
Singapore 536196

Panpac Education

Email: panpmktg@panpaceducation.com
Website: http://www.panpaceducation.com

EPB Pan Pacific is a trademark of Times Publishing Limited

ISBN 978-981-280-660-4

First published 2009
Reprinted 2009

Printed by Times Graphics Pte Ltd

Foreword

Mathematics plays an important role in the development of a nation and its people. At the individual level, mathematics underpins many aspects of our everyday activities, from making sense of information in the newspaper to making decisions about personal finances. It supports learning in many fields of study, whether it is the sciences or humanities. A good understanding of basic mathematics is essential wherever calculations, measurements, graphical interpretations and statistical analyses are necessary. At the national level, a strong grounding in mathematics is essential to support an innovation and technology driven economy.

In Singapore, a substantial amount of curriculum time is devoted to the teaching and learning of mathematics in the early grade levels to build a strong foundation for the acquisition of mathematics knowledge and skills in later years. However, providing curriculum time alone is not enough. Effective learning of mathematics requires a coherent and well structured syllabus, excellent instructional materials, and good teachers who use sound pedagogical strategies that are developmentally appropriate.

This Monograph is about the Singapore Model Method – a pedagogical strategy that was developed by a team of curriculum specialists in the Singapore Ministry of Education in the early 1980s. The Primary Mathematics Project team led by Dr Kho Tek Hong was tasked to develop a set of instructional materials to improve the mathematics attainment of the students in a young nation. Today, the Model Method and its ubiquitous bar diagrams are perhaps the most recognised features of the Singapore mathematics curriculum.

The Model Method has helped in developing our students' proficiency in mathematics, as attested by our achievements in Trends in Mathematics and Science Studies (TIMSS) 1995, 1999 and 2003. The TIMSS results affirmed not just the strength and robustness of our mathematics curriculum but also the dedication and hard work of our teachers and students in the teaching and learning of mathematics.

Our Mathematics Curriculum Framework remains focused on mathematical problem solving and will continue to emphasise conceptual understanding, skills proficiency, learning of process skills, metacognition, and the development of a positive attitude towards mathematics. While this framework has served us well we will continue to evolve our mathematics curriculum so that it remains up-to-date and relevant for 21st century learners.

In sharing our experience in developing our mathematics curriculum we hope to have made a contribution to the community of mathematics educators.

Miss Seah Jiak Choo
Director-General of Education
Ministry of Education Singapore

About The Authors

Kho Tek Hong, Ph. D. was a Principal Curriculum Specialist in the Curriculum Planning and Development Division of the Ministry of Education, Singapore. He was the Project Director of the Primary Mathematics Project (PMP) from 1980 to 1996. The PMP team was tasked to produce instructional materials for primary mathematics. The Concrete-Pictorial-Abstract approach and the Model Method, developed by the team in the 1980s to help students visualise and conceptualise abstract concepts and relationships in Mathematics, have been proven successful and are still in use today. After his retirement in 2007, Dr Kho continues to work part-time with the Ministry of Education as a consultant in mathematics education.

Yeo Shu Mei, Ph. D. is a Curriculum Planning Officer in the Ministry of Education, Singapore. Her current work involves the development of the mathematics curriculum, teacher training, educational research, and review and design of instructional materials. She began her career as a junior college mathematics teacher and has more than 10 years of teaching experience before joining the Centre for Research in Pedagogy and Practice (CRPP) as a Research Associate in 2003. She has taught in teaching programmes like the Postgraduate Diploma Degree of Education (PGDE) as well as the Master of Education (MEd) at the National Institute of Education. She was part of the editorial team for *Series on Mathematics Education Vol. 1: How Chinese Learn Mathematics: Perspectives from Insiders* as well as a secondary mathematics textbook published locally.

James Lim, MA (Ed.) is a mathematics teacher in the Integrated Programme of a junior college in Singapore, having recently returned from the US after completing his Masters in Mathematics Education. He began his career teaching A-Level mathematics at the junior college in 2003, but subsequently developed a passion for secondary level mathematics through his involvement in the school's integrated programme and a short stint at the Curriculum Planning and Development Division. His postgraduate experiences in exploring mathematics learning at the secondary level in the areas of cognition, pedagogy, curriculum, and teacher professionalism have served to strengthen his interest and affirm his belief in the importance of quality mathematics education.

Reviewers

Acknowledgements

We would like to acknowledge the following for their contributions to this publication:

Ms Seah Jiak Choo, Director-General of Education for her Foreword;

Ms Ho Peng, Director of Curriculum Planning and Development Division and Mdm Low Khah Gek, Deputy Director, Sciences Branch for their support and encouragement;

The team of reviewers for their valuable feedback;

Dr Lee Peng Yee and Ms Christina Cheong Ngan Peng for their advice and input;

Mrs Wang-Tang Suet Yen and Mdm Goh Lung Eng Esther for reading and commenting on the final draft; and all who made this publication possible.

About This Monograph

This monograph serves as a resource book on the Model Method. The main purpose is to make explicit how the Model Method is used to develop students' understanding of fundamental mathematics concepts and proficiency in solving basic mathematics word problems. Through the construction of a pictorial model to represent the known and unknown quantities and their relationships in a problem, students gain better understanding of the problem and develop their abilities in mathematical thinking and problem solving. This will provide a strong foundation for the learning of mathematics from the primary to secondary levels and beyond.

This monograph also features the Mathematics Framework of the Singapore mathematics curriculum, and discusses the changes that it has undergone over the past two decades. These changes reflected the changing emphases, needs and challenges in the mathematics curriculum as we entered the 21st century.

The monograph is organised into seven chapters.
- Chapter 1 provides an overview of the Mathematics Framework and the Model Method as key features of the Singapore mathematics curriculum.
- Chapter 2 highlights the evolution of the Mathematics Framework over the last two decades.
- Chapters 3 and 4 illustrate the use of pictorial models in the development of the concepts of the four operations as well as fraction, ratio and percentage.
- Chapter 5 explains and discusses how the Model Method is used for solving structurally complex word problems at the primary level.
- Chapter 6 illustrates how the Model Method can be integrated with the algebraic method to formulate algebraic equations for solving problems.
- Chapter 7 concludes the monograph by discussing some perspectives of problem solving that account for the success of the Model Method, and the connection between the Model Method and the algebraic method.

Contents

1

Introduction

Since the independence of Singapore in 1965, the education system has undergone several reforms. The first major reform was the New Education System (Primary and Secondary) in the late 1970s, which aimed to provide all students with at least ten years of general education. Mathematics was compulsory up to the end of secondary education, and streaming by ability was introduced. Different curricula for different streams and courses were designed to meet the varying needs and abilities of the students (Soh, 2005, 2008).

In 1975, the Ministry of Education, conducted a survey to investigate the mathematics attainment of primary students. The report "Attainment of Basic Numeracy and Literacy Skills by Pupils with Primary Education" revealed that at least 25% of Primary 6 students did not meet the minimum numeracy level. Also, in 1981, diagnostic tests on the basic skills of mathematics were administered to a sample of more than 17 000 Primary 1 to 4 students. The results revealed that more than 50% of the Primary 3 and 4 students performed poorly on items that tested division. 87% of the Primary 2 to 4 students could solve problems when key words like 'altogether' or 'left' were given, but only 46% of them could solve problems without key words. These indicated that primary school students had not mastered the basic skills of mathematics, and the concern of low attainment in mathematics was a call for a major review of the mathematics syllabus, teaching approaches and instructional materials (MOE, 1979, 1981; Cheong, 2002).

The establishment of the Curriculum Development Institute of Singapore (CDIS) in June 1980 was an important milestone. Among the various project teams, the Primary Mathematics Project (PMP) team, led by Dr Kho Tek Hong, was tasked to produce instructional materials for the teaching and learning of primary mathematics with effective teaching approaches and professional development of teachers. The PMP instructional materials advocated the Concrete-Pictorial-Abstract approach. In this approach, students were provided with the necessary learning experiences and meaningful contexts, using concrete manipulatives and pictorial representations, to help them learn abstract mathematics (CDIS, 1987; Yip & Sim, 1990; Ang, 2008).

The Model Method for problem solving, as it is commonly known in Singapore, was an innovation in the teaching and learning of mathematics developed by the project team in the 1980s to address the issue of students having great difficulty with word problems in the early years of primary school. It has since become a distinguishing feature of the Singapore primary mathematics curriculum. This approach entails students drawing a pictorial model to represent mathematical quantities (known and unknown) and their relationships (part-whole and comparison) given in a problem, to help them visualise and solve the problem. The main concepts in this approach, the part-whole and comparison models, are also used to illustrate the concepts of fraction, ratio and percentage (Kho, 1987). Recently, the Model Method has been integrated with the algebraic method at the secondary school level to help students formulate algebraic equations to solve problems. This would bridge the learning of primary and secondary mathematics, from the arithmetic method to the algebraic method (Kho, 2005, 2007).

In the 1990s, Singapore's education system was reviewed and realigned to meet the challenges of the new century. The emphasis was on upgrading and providing quality education for all students. There was a shift in paradigm from an efficiency-driven education to an ability-driven one. The mathematics curriculum was revised in 1990 to stress the importance of both the processes and products in mathematics learning. This resulted in the production of the Mathematics Framework, which became another important feature of Singapore's mathematics education. The framework articulates and explicates the intention of mathematics education, and provides guidance in the teaching, learning, and assessment of mathematics. The goal was to develop an effective mathematics curriculum that will enable all students to learn and apply mathematics. The Mathematics Framework has been updated during the subsequent revisions of the mathematics curriculum in 2000 and 2003 to reflect the changing emphases and needs such as the infusion of three initiatives, namely, Thinking Skills, Information Technology, and National Education, into the curriculum (Goh & Gopinathan, 2008; Soh, 2005, 2008; MOE, 1990, 2000, 2006).

The Mathematics Framework and the Model Method are key features of the Singapore mathematics curriculum. Both have received increasing attention since Singapore emerged first in TIMSS[+] in 1995, and subsequently in 1999 and 2003. This monograph is intended to provide an insightful account of the ideas and developments of the Mathematics Framework and the Model Method. It will be of interest to mathematics teachers and researchers who want to gain a better understanding of the Singapore mathematics curriculum.

[+]*TIMSS was known as Third International Mathematics and Science Study in 1995 and 1999. It was renamed Trends in International Mathematics and Science Study in 2003.*

2

Mathematics Framework of the Singapore Mathematics Curriculum

The Singapore mathematics curriculum is guided by the Mathematics Framework (see Figure 2.1) which encapsulates our aim to develop students' mathematical abilities, in particular their problem-solving abilities. The framework was introduced in 1990 in the primary and lower secondary mathematics syllabuses, and was extended formally to all levels in 2003. It has undergone some changes during the curriculum reviews in 2000 and 2003, reflecting the new educational emphases in a rapidly changing, highly competitive and technologically driven world. See Notes 2.1 on page 10 for the original framework (1990) and the first revision (2000). Amidst the revisions, the focus has remained on solving problems mathematically (MOE, 1990, 2000, 2006).

The Mathematics Framework shows the underlying principles of an effective mathematics programme that is applicable to all levels, from the primary to advanced levels. It sets the direction for the teaching, learning, and assessment of mathematics.

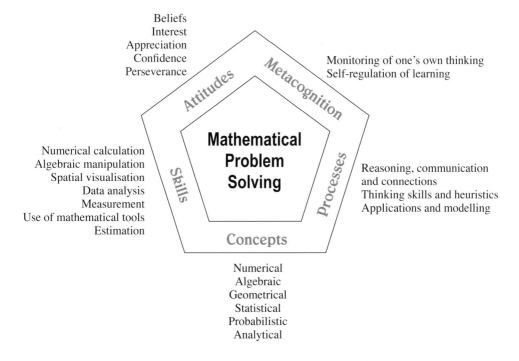

Figure 2.1   Singapore Mathematics Framework (2003)

Mathematical problem solving is central to mathematics learning. It involves the acquisition and application of mathematics concepts and skills in a wide range of situations, including non-routine, open-ended and real-world problems. The development of mathematical problem-solving ability is dependent on five inter-related components, namely, *Concepts*, *Skills*, *Processes*, *Attitudes,* and *Metacognition.*

The *Concepts* and *Skills* Components

Mathematical concepts cover numerical, algebraic, geometrical, statistical, probabilistic, and analytical concepts. Students should develop and explore the mathematics ideas in depth, and see that mathematics is an integrated whole, not merely isolated pieces of knowledge. They should be given a variety of learning experiences to help them develop a deep understanding of mathematical concepts, and to make sense of various mathematical ideas, as well as their connections and applications, in order to participate actively in learning mathematics and to become more confident in exploring and applying mathematics. These include the use of manipulatives (concrete materials), practical work, and technological aids.

Mathematical skills include procedural skills for numerical calculation, algebraic manipulation, spatial visualisation, data analysis, measurement, use of mathematical tools, and estimation. The development of skills proficiencies in students is essential in the learning and application of mathematics. Although students should become competent in the various mathematical skills, over-emphasising procedural skills without understanding the underlying mathematical principles should be avoided. Skills proficiencies include the ability to use technology, where appropriate, for exploration and problem solving. It is important also to incorporate the use of thinking skills and heuristics in the process of the development of skills proficiencies.

Mathematics education in Singapore places importance on the acquisition and application of mathematics concepts and skills. These are carefully planned and explicitly set out as mathematics content students need to learn for each grade level, so that they are ready for the next level of learning. The content is deepened progressively through a spiral approach. There are desirable learning outcomes and specific competencies that students should achieve at various stages of schooling. Some changes in the *Concepts* and *Skills* components of the Mathematics Framework have been made since its introduction in 1990. During the curriculum review in 2003, the Mathematics Framework was extended to upper secondary and advanced levels. The "Probabilistic" and "Analytical" concepts were included to reflect the importance of mathematics in dealing with situations that involve uncertainty and change. Under the Skills component, due emphasis was given to "Spatial visualisation" and "Measurement" skills. This signals the importance of providing practical learning experiences and opportunities for exploring geometry in real-life.

The *Processes* Component

Mathematical processes refer to the knowledge skills (or process skills) involved in the process of acquiring and applying mathematical knowledge, including reasoning, communication and connections, thinking skills and heuristics, and applications and modelling.

Reasoning, Communication and Connections

Mathematical reasoning refers to the ability to analyse mathematical situations and construct logical arguments. It is a habit of mind that can be developed through the applications of mathematics in different contexts. Communication refers to the ability to use mathematical language to express mathematical ideas and arguments precisely, concisely and logically. It helps students develop their own understanding of mathematics and sharpen their mathematical thinking. Connections refer to the ability to see and make linkages among mathematical ideas, between mathematics and other subjects, and between mathematics and everyday life. This helps students make sense of what they learn in mathematics. Mathematical reasoning, communication and connections should pervade all levels of mathematics learning, from the primary to advanced levels.

Thinking Skills and Heuristics

Students should use various thinking skills and heuristics to help them solve mathematical problems. Thinking skills are skills that can be used in a thinking process, such as classifying, comparing, sequencing, analysing parts and whole, identifying patterns and relationships, induction, deduction and spatial visualisation. Heuristics are what students can do to approach a problem when the solution to the problem is not obvious. Some examples of heuristics are listed below in four categories according to how they are used:

- To give a representation, e.g. draw a diagram, make a list, use equations;
- To make a calculated guess, e.g. guess and check, look for patterns, make suppositions;
- To go through the process, e.g. act it out, work backwards, before-after; and
- To change the problem, e.g. restate the problem, simplify the problem, solve part of the problem.

Applications and Modelling

Applications and modelling play an important role in the development of mathematical understanding and competencies. Students should apply mathematical problem-solving skills and reasoning skills to tackle a variety of problems, including open-ended and real-world problems. Mathematical modelling is the process of formulating and improving a mathematical model to represent and solve real-world problems. Through mathematical modelling, students learn to use a variety of representations of data, and to select and apply appropriate mathematical methods and tools in solving real-world problems. The opportunity to deal with empirical data and use mathematical tools for data analysis should be part of the learning at all levels.

From its inception in 1990, the Mathematics Framework has placed due emphasis on mathematical processes following the trends in mathematics education in the USA and the UK in the 1980s (see Notes 2.2, p. 11), where there was a shift in emphasis from the product aspect – what mathematics content should be taught and learned, to the process aspect – how the content should be best taught and learned. While the acquisition and application of mathematics concepts and skills are still the main goals of mathematics education, mathematical processes enable students to develop thinking and problem-solving skills (Kho, 1989). In the 2000 Mathematics Framework, "Deductive reasoning" and "Inductive reasoning" were encapsulated in "Thinking skills" (see Notes 2.1, p. 10; Notes 2.3, p. 12). Two new dimensions: "Reasoning, communication and connections" and "Applications and modelling" were included in the 2003 Mathematics Framework to highlight the importance of these processes to meet the challenges of the 21st century. "Communication", originally in the Skills component, was then presented in a three-way relationship with "Reasoning" and "Connections" to signal a focus on encouraging student-centred, active and collaborative learning. Students should be given the opportunity to explore and solve real-world problems with the use of technology.

The *Metacognition* Component

Metacognition, or "thinking about thinking", refers to the awareness of, and the ability to control one's thinking processes, in particular the selection and use of problem-solving strategies. It includes monitoring of one's own thinking, and self-regulation of learning. The provision of metacognitive experience is necessary to help students develop their problem-solving abilities. The following strategies may be used to develop the metacognitive awareness of students and to enrich their metacognitive experience:

- Expose students to general problem-solving skills, thinking skills and heuristics, and how these skills can be applied to solve problems;
- Encourage students to think aloud the strategies and methods they use to solve particular problems;

8

- Provide students with problems that require planning (before solving) and evaluation (after solving);
- Encourage students to seek alternative ways of solving the same problem and to check the appropriateness and reasonableness of answers; and
- Allow students to discuss how to solve a particular problem and to explain the different methods that they can use for solving the problem.

As reflected in the 2003 Mathematics Framework, *Metacognition* embraces two aspects. The monitoring aspect ("Monitoring of one's own thinking") requires students to know the metacognitive strategies, and when and how to use them. The control aspect ("Self-regulation of learning") requires students to keep track of how things are going and make changes when necessary (Wong, 2002). The introduction of "Self-regulation of learning" is to enhance students' problem-solving abilities.

The *Attitudes* Component

Attitudes refer to the affective aspects of mathematics learning such as:

- Beliefs about mathematics and its usefulness;
- Interest and enjoyment in learning mathematics;
- Appreciation of the beauty and power of mathematics;
- Confidence in using mathematics; and
- Perseverance in solving a problem.

Students' attitudes towards mathematics are shaped by their learning experiences. Making the learning of mathematics fun, meaningful and relevant goes a long way to inculcating positive attitudes towards the subject. Care and attention should be given to the design of learning activities to build confidence in and develop appreciation for the subject.

"Perseverance" was added in the 2000 Mathematics Framework in light of emerging non-routine problems and open-ended problems which require students to investigate and solve using a wide range of heuristics. This is an important quality. Students with perseverance will not give up easily when they encounter difficulties in solving a problem. The 2003 Mathematics Framework widened the range of affective dimensions to include "Beliefs". Students' beliefs about mathematics and its usefulness can influence their attitudes in mathematics learning and problem solving. This dimension is desirable for student-centred learning where students are encouraged to take on more responsibility for their own learning.

The five components of the Mathematics Framework are integral parts of mathematics learning and problem solving in the Singapore mathematics curriculum. They are comparable to the five strands of mathematical proficiency identified in the USA, namely, *Conceptual understanding*, *Procedural fluency*, *Strategic competence*, *Adaptive reasoning* and *Productive disposition* (AIR, 2005) (see Notes 2.4, p. 13). This affirms our effort to provide a more engaging, student-centred, and technology-supported learning environment, and to promote greater diversity and creativity in learning.

Notes

2.1 The Singapore Mathematics Framework has undergone some refinement since its introduction in 1990. The original framework (1990) and the first revision (2000) are given here for reference purpose.

Singapore Mathematics Framework (1990)

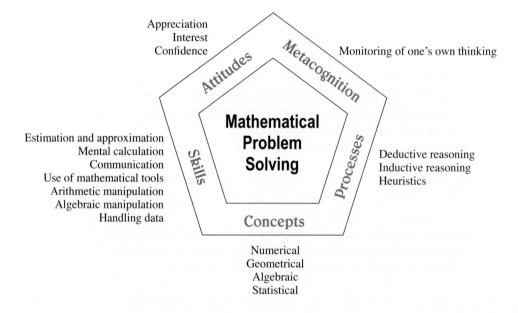

Singapore Mathematics Framework (2000)

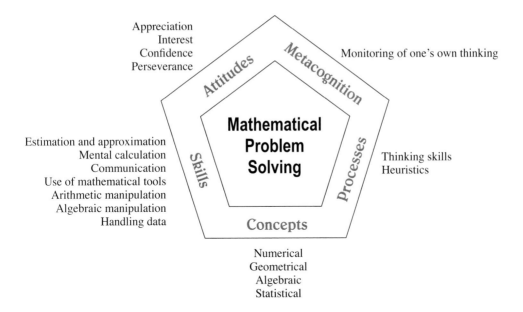

2.2 In 1980, the National Council of Teachers of Mathematics (NCTM) of the USA published an important document entitled *An Agenda for Action: Recommendations for School Mathematics of the 1980s*. It recognised the importance of problem-solving skills in mathematics, and recommended that problem solving be the focus of school mathematics in the 1980s (NCTM, 1980).

In the UK, *The Cockcroft Report of the Committee of Enquiry into the Teaching of Mathematics in Schools* also pointed out that problem solving was one dimension lacking in the mathematics classroom, and emphasised the importance of problem solving and investigation (Department of Education and Science, 1982).

2.3 The following are suggested thinking skills and heuristics for problem solving listed in the primary and lower secondary mathematics syllabuses.

Thinking Skills
Classifying
Comparing
Sequencing
Analysing parts and whole
Identifying patterns and relationships
Induction
Deduction
Generalising
Verifying
Spatial visualisation
Heuristics for Problem Solving
Act it out
Use a diagram/ model
Make a systematic list
Look for pattern(s)
Work backwards
Use before-after concept
Use guess and check
Make suppositions
Restate the problem in another way
Simplify the problem
Solve part of the problem
Thinking of a related problem
Use equations

2.4 The USA report, *Adding It Up: Helping Children Learn Mathematics*, identifies five strands of mathematical proficiency, namely, *Conceptual understanding*, *Procedural fluency*, *Strategic competence*, *Adaptive reasoning, and Productive disposition* (RAND Mathematics Study Panel, 2003; National Research Council, 2001). The five strands map closely to the five components of the Singapore Mathematics Framework as shown in the following table.

Mathematics Framework (Singapore)	Mathematical Proficiency (USA)
Concepts – numerical, algebraic, geometrical, statistical, probabilistic, and analytical concepts	*Conceptual understanding* – comprehension of mathematical concepts, operations, and relations
Skills – procedural skills for numerical calculation, algebraic manipulation, spatial visualisation, data analysis, measurement, use of mathematical tools, and estimation	*Procedural fluency* – skill in carrying out procedures flexibly, accurately, efficiently, and appropriately
Processes – knowledge skills (or process skills) involved in the process of acquiring and applying mathematical knowledge • reasoning, communication and connections • thinking skills and heuristics • applications and modelling	*Strategic competence* – ability to formulate, represent, and solve mathematical problems
Metacognition – awareness of, and the ability to control one's thinking processes • monitoring of one's own thinking • self-regulation of learning	*Adaptive reasoning* – capacity for logical thought, reflection, explanation, and justification
Attitudes – affective aspects of mathematics learning such as • beliefs about mathematics and its usefulness • interest and enjoyment in learning mathematics • appreciation of the beauty and power of mathematics • confidence in using mathematics • perseverance in solving a problem	*Productive disposition* – habitual inclination to see mathematics as sensible, useful, and worthwhile, coupled with a belief in diligence and one's own efficacy

3

Model Method and Concepts of the Four Operations

The Singapore primary mathematics curriculum places great emphasis on quantitative relationships when students learn the concepts of numbers and the four operations. A key feature is the development and use of the Model Method since the 1980s.

In this chapter, we discuss how the Model Method is used to illustrate the concepts of the four operations, and to solve related word problems. The original paper presented by Dr Kho Tek Hong at the 4th Southeast Asian Conference on Mathematical Education (Kho, 1987) is reproduced at Appendix A on page 74.

The Part-Whole and Comparison Models

The introduction of the part-whole and comparison models is an essential element of the concrete-pictorial-abstract approach of the Singapore primary mathematics curriculum. Students make use of concrete objects to make sense of the part-whole and comparison concepts. Then they progress to the drawing of rectangular bars as pictorial representations of the models, and use the models to help them solve abstract mathematics word problems.

The Part-Whole Model

Consider the following problem:

Ali has 8 toy cars. David has 6 toy cars. How many toy cars do they have altogether?

In Primary One, students use concrete objects (or picture cut-outs) to form two groups of toy cars, and put the two groups together:

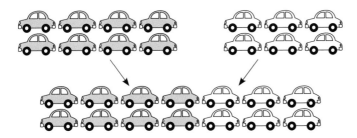

They add the two numbers 8 and 6 to give the total number. Then they write the arithmetic equation 8 + 6 = 14 to solve the problem.

In Primary Two, students may draw a pictorial model to represent the problem situation, e.g.

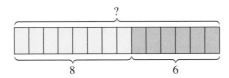

The model can be visualised as a whole comprising two parts. Students add the two parts to find the whole:

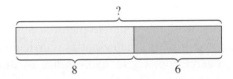

$8 + 6 = 14$

They have 14 toy cars altogether.

In the part-whole model (also known as the part-part-whole model), there is a quantitative relationship among the three quantities: the whole and two parts.

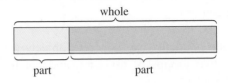

To find the whole given two parts, students add:

part + part = whole

When the whole and one part are given, to find the other part, students subtract:

whole − part = part

The Comparison Model

Consider another problem:

There are 2 more pears than oranges. If there are 6 pears, how many oranges are there?

A young child may count with concrete objects (or picture cut-outs) to reason out the answer. In Primary One, students are required to write the arithmetic equation $6 - 2 = 4$ to solve the problem. This is abstract, and many students have difficulty writing the arithmetic equation.

To make sense of the comparison concept that "there are 2 more pears than oranges", students are asked to match the pears and oranges one to one to compare their numbers. For example:

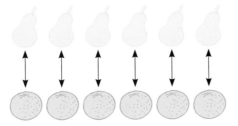

There are 6 pears. There are as many pears as oranges.
(The two numbers are equal.)

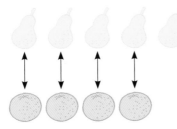

There are 6 pears. There are 2 more pears than oranges.
(The difference between the two numbers is 2.)

In Primary Two, students may draw a pictorial model to represent the problem situation, e.g.

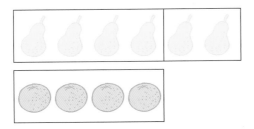

This is the comparison model:

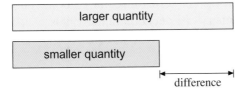

The comparison model is used to compare two quantities to show how much one quantity is greater (or smaller) than the other. Without the model, students may simply rely on the cue words "more than" and use addition to solve the problem without realising that it is incorrect. There is a quantitative relationship among the three quantities: larger quantity, smaller quantity, and the difference. The difference is obtained by subtracting the smaller quantity from the larger quantity. That is,

larger quantity – smaller quantity = difference

To find the larger quantity given the smaller quantity and the difference, students add:

smaller quantity + difference = larger quantity

When the larger quantity and the difference are given, to find the smaller quantity, students subtract:

larger quantity – difference = smaller quantity

For example, students draw the following model to solve the comparison problem given on page 16.

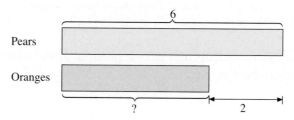

$6 - 2 = 4$

There are 4 oranges.

Concepts of the Four Operations

In the following sections, examples are based on the Primary Mathematics textbook series (second edition), published by the Singapore Ministry of Education in the 1990s.

1. Part-Whole Model (Addition and Subtraction)

The following examples illustrate the part-whole concepts of addition and subtraction.

Example 1 (Primary 3A⁺)

134 boys and 119 girls took part in an art competition. How many children took part in the competition?

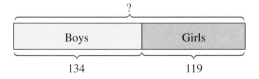

Here a bar is drawn to represent the whole (total number of children). It is divided into two parts, representing the number of boys (134) and the number of girls (119) respectively. From the model, students can find the whole (shown by the symbol ?) by adding the two parts.

$$134 + 119 = 253$$

253 children took part in the art competition.

Example 2

253 children took part in an art competition. If there were 134 boys, how many girls were there?

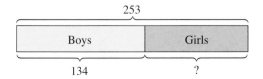

In this example, the whole and one part (the number of boys) are given. The other part (the number of girls) can be found by subtracting the given part (134) from the whole (253).

$$253 - 134 = 119$$

There were 119 girls.

⁺ *The examples in Chapters 3, 4 and 5 are taken from the Primary Mathematics textbook series (second edition), published by the Singapore Ministry of Education in the 1990s.*

2. Comparison Model (Addition and Subtraction)

This section deals with the comparison concepts of addition and subtraction.

Example 3 (Primary 3A)

Meilin saved $184. Betty saved $63 less than Meilin. How much did Betty save?

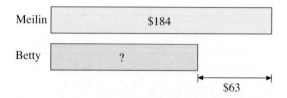

Here two bars are drawn to represent Meilin's savings and Betty's savings. In the comparison model, one bar is longer than the other, showing that Meilin saved more than Betty. From the model, students can find the smaller quantity by subtracting the difference ($63) from the larger quantity ($184).

$$184 - 63 = 121$$

Betty saved $121.

Example 4

Betty saved $121. She saved $63 less than Meilin. How much did Meilin save?

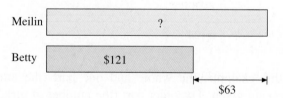

In this example, the smaller quantity (Betty's savings) and the difference are given. The larger quantity (Meilin's savings) can be found by adding the smaller quantity ($121) and the difference ($63).

$$121 + 63 = 184$$

Meilin saved $184.

Example 5

Meilin saved $184. Betty saved $121. How much less than Meilin did Betty save?

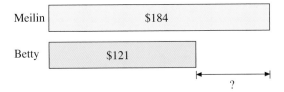

In this example, both quantities are given. Subtracting the smaller quantity ($121) from the larger quantity ($184) gives the difference.

$$184 - 121 = 63$$

Betty saved $63 less than Meilin.

3. Part-Whole Model (Multiplication and Division)

This section deals with the part-whole concepts of multiplication and division. It involves a whole divided into a number of equal parts. For example, the following model shows a whole divided into 3 equal parts.

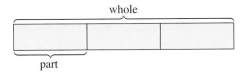

There is a quantitative relationship among the three quantities: the whole, one part, and the number of parts. To find the whole given one part and the number of parts, students multiply:

one part × number of parts = whole

To find one part given the whole and the number of parts, students divide:

whole ÷ number of parts = one part

To find the number of parts given the whole and one part, students divide:

whole ÷ one part = number of parts

Example 6 (Primary 3A)

5 children shared the cost of a present equally. Each of them paid $6. What was the cost of the present?

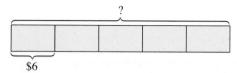

Here a bar is drawn to represent the whole (cost of the present). It is divided into 5 equal parts, each representing $6. From the model, students can find the whole by multiplying one part ($6) and the number of parts (5).

$5 \times 6 = 30$

The cost of the present was $30.

Example 7

5 children bought a present for $30. They shared the cost equally. How much did each child pay?

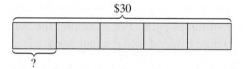

In this example, knowing the whole and the number of parts, students can find one part by dividing the whole ($30) by the number of parts (5).

$30 \div 5 = 6$

Each child paid $6.

Example 8

A group of children bought a present for $30. They paid $6 each. How many children were there in the group?

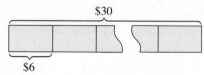

The broken section in the bar indicates that the number of parts is unknown. Knowing the whole and one part, students can find the number of parts by dividing the whole ($30) by one part ($6).

$30 \div 6 = 5$

There were 5 children in the group.

4. Comparison Model (Multiplication and Division)

This section deals with the comparison concepts of multiplication and division. Here two quantities are compared such that one quantity is a multiple of the other. For example, the following model shows two quantities, the larger quantity being 5 times the smaller quantity.

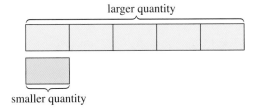

There is a quantitative relationship among the three quantities: larger quantity, smaller quantity, and the multiple. The multiple is obtained by dividing the larger quantity by the smaller quantity. That is,

larger quantity ÷ smaller quantity = multiple

To find the larger quantity given the smaller quantity and the multiple, students multiply:

smaller quantity × multiple = larger quantity

To find the smaller quantity given the larger quantity and the multiple, students divide:

larger quantity ÷ multiple = smaller quantity

Example 9 (Primary 3A)

A farmer has 7 ducks. He has 5 times as many chickens as ducks. How many chickens does the farmer have?

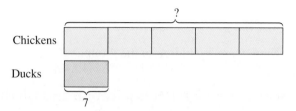

Here two bars, of lengths 5 units and 1 unit, are drawn to represent the number of chickens and the number of ducks respectively. The model shows that the number of chickens is 5 times the number of ducks. Given the number of ducks (1 unit = 7), students can find the number of chickens (5 units) by multiplication.

$5 \times 7 = 35$

The farmer has 35 chickens.

Example 10

A farmer has 35 chickens. He has 5 times as many chickens as ducks. How many ducks does the farmer have?

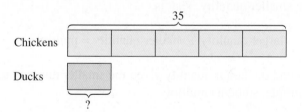

In this example, given the number of chickens (5 units = 35), students can find the number of ducks (1 unit) by division.

$35 \div 5 = 7$

The farmer has 7 ducks.

Example 11

A farmer has 7 ducks and 35 chickens. How many times as many chickens as ducks does the farmer have?

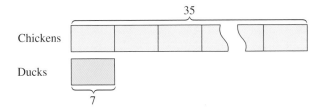

The broken section in the longer bar indicates that the number of units is unknown. Given the two quantities, students can find the multiple by division.

$35 \div 7 = 5$

The farmer has 5 times as many chickens as ducks.

Problem Structures

With the Model Method, we are able to study the problem structures of various word problems. The model shows explicitly the problem structure, and the known and unknown quantities (whole numbers, fractions, or decimals) involved in a problem. It provides a visual tool that enables students to determine what operation (addition, subtraction, multiplication, or division) to use to solve the problem. An analysis of problem structures of word problems involving the concepts of the four operations is given in Appendix B on page 82.

4

Model Method and Concepts of Fraction, Ratio and Percentage

In this chapter, we discuss the use of the Model Method to illustrate the concepts of fraction, ratio and percentage, and to solve related word problems. An analysis of problem structures is given in Appendix B on page 82.

I.   Fraction

Part-Whole Model (Fraction)

The part-whole model illustrates the part-whole concept of fraction. A fraction represents a part of a whole. The fraction notation tells how much of a whole it represents. For example, when a whole (1 unit) is divided into 4 equal parts, the fraction $\frac{1}{4}$ represents 1 out of the 4 equal parts (i.e. $\frac{1}{4}$ unit). The fraction $\frac{3}{4}$ represents 3 out of the 4 equal parts (i.e. $\frac{3}{4}$ unit).

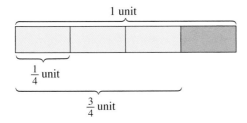

Here the two fractions $\frac{1}{4}$ and $\frac{3}{4}$ are based on the same whole. ($\frac{3}{4}$ means $\frac{1}{4} + \frac{1}{4} + \frac{1}{4}$, or $3 \times \frac{1}{4}$)

A fraction can also be related to division. For example, $\frac{3}{4}$ can be interpreted as $3 \div 4$. That is, when a whole representing 3 units is divided into 4 equal parts, each part is $\frac{3}{4}$ unit.

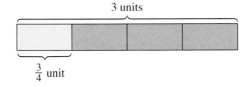

The part-whole model can be used to solve problems involving fraction. For example, the following model shows $\frac{3}{4}$ of the whole:

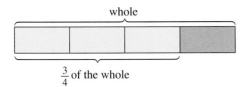

27

The fraction $\frac{3}{4}$ means 3 units out of 4 units. The whole represents the total number, or the total value. It can be a whole number, a fraction, or a decimal. For example, if the whole represents 12 objects, the number of objects in $\frac{3}{4}$ of the whole can be found as follows:

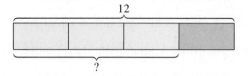

4 units = 12

1 unit $= \frac{12}{4} = 3$

3 units = 3 × 3 = 9

There are 9 objects in $\frac{3}{4}$ of the whole.

Conversely, if it is given that $\frac{3}{4}$ of the whole is 9, the whole can be found as follows:

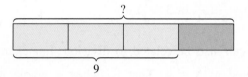

3 units = 9

1 unit $= \frac{9}{3} = 3$

4 units = 4 × 3 = 12

There are 12 objects in the whole set.

Example 1 (Primary 4B)

Salmah bought 24 flowers. $\frac{2}{3}$ of them were white. How many white flowers were there?

28

Here the part-whole model is used to illustrate $\frac{2}{3}$ of the whole. The fraction $\frac{2}{3}$ means 2 units out of 3 units.

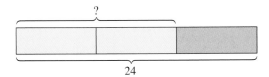

To find the number of white flowers (2 units), students find the value of 1 unit first:

3 units = 24

1 unit $= \frac{24}{3} = 8$

2 units $= 2 \times 8 = 16$

There were 16 white flowers.

Comparison Model (Fraction)

The comparison model illustrates the comparison concept of fraction. The following model shows two quantities A and B which are 5 units and 1 unit respectively:

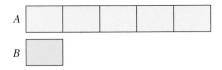

If B is taken as the base, and A is compared relative to B, then:

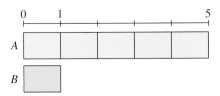

A is 5 times as much as B.

This relationship can also be expressed as:

A is 5 times B. $(A = 5 \times B)$

29

Conversely, if A is taken as the base, and B is compared relative to A, then:

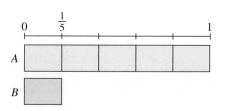

B is $\dfrac{1}{5}$ as much as A. (The fraction $\dfrac{1}{5}$ means 1 unit to 5 units.)

This relationship can also be expressed as:

B is $\dfrac{1}{5}$ of A.

B is $\dfrac{1}{5}$ times A. $(B = \dfrac{1}{5} \times A)$

Again, the following model shows two quantities P and Q which are 5 units and 3 units respectively:

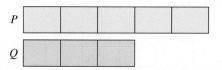

If P is taken as the base, and Q is compared relative to P, then:

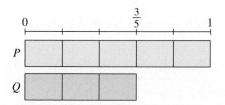

Q is $\dfrac{3}{5}$ as much as P. (The fraction $\dfrac{3}{5}$ means 3 units to 5 units.)

This relationship can also be expressed as:

Q is $\dfrac{3}{5}$ of P.

Q is $\dfrac{3}{5}$ times P. $(Q = \dfrac{3}{5} \times P)$

Conversely, if Q is taken as the base, and P is compared relative to Q, then:

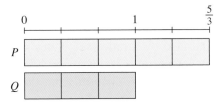

P is $\frac{5}{3}$ as much as Q. (The fraction $\frac{5}{3}$ means 5 units to 3 units.)

This relationship can also be expressed as:

P is $\frac{5}{3}$ of Q.

P is $\frac{5}{3}$ times Q. ($P = \frac{5}{3} \times Q$)

Given one quantity P or Q, students can find the other quantity as exemplified below.

Example 2 (Primary 6A)

There are $\frac{3}{5}$ as many boys as girls. If there are 75 girls, how many boys are there?

Here the comparison model illustrates that there are $\frac{3}{5}$ as many boys as girls. The fraction $\frac{3}{5}$ means 3 units to 5 units.

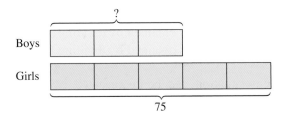

Given the number of girls (5 units), students can find the number of boys (3 units) using the unitary method (i.e. finding the value of 1 unit first).

5 units = 75

1 unit $= \dfrac{75}{5} = 15$

3 units = 3 × 15 = 45

There are 45 boys.

31

II. Ratio

Comparison Model (Ratio)

Two quantities can be compared by a difference, by a multiple, by a fraction, and also by a ratio (see Notes 4.1, p. 40). In this section, the concept of ratio is discussed. To compare two or more quantities by a ratio, the quantities must be expressed in the same units. For example,

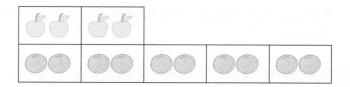

Here 1 unit = 2. The numbers of apples and oranges are 2 units and 5 units respectively.

> The ratio of the number of apples to the number of oranges is 2 : 5. (The ratio 2 : 5 means 2 units to 5 units.)

> The ratio of the number of oranges to the number of apples is 5 : 2. (The ratio 5 : 2 means 5 units to 2 units.)

In this example, students can write the ratio of the number of apples to the number of oranges as 4 : 10, and then simplify it to 2 : 5. That is,

$$\frac{\text{Number of apples}}{\text{Number of oranges}} = \frac{4}{10} = \frac{2}{5}$$

Given two quantities A and B, the ratio of A to B is not the same as the ratio of B to A.

> The ratio of A to B is obtained by dividing A by B.
> The ratio of B to A is obtained by dividing B by A.

The problem situation can be represented by the comparison model:

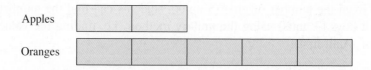

The model shows that the ratio of the number of apples to the number of oranges is 2 : 5. The number of apples and the number of oranges are 2 units and 5 units respectively.

Given the number of apples (2 units), students can find the number of oranges (5 units):

2 units = 4

1 unit $= \dfrac{4}{2} = 2$

5 units $= 5 \times 2 = 10$

There are 10 oranges.

Conversely, given the number of oranges (5 units), students can find the number of apples (2 units):

5 units = 10

1 unit $= \dfrac{10}{5} = 2$

2 units $= 2 \times 2 = 4$

There are 4 apples.

Example 3 (Primary 5A)

The ratio of the number of pies to the number of cakes to the number of buns is 3 : 1 : 4. If there are 30 pies, how many buns are there?

Here three bars are drawn to represent the number of pies (3 units), cakes (1 unit) and buns (4 units) respectively. The comparison model shows the ratio 3 : 1 : 4.

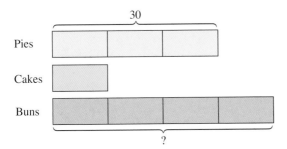

Given the number of pies (3 units), students can find the number of buns (4 units) using the unitary method:

3 units = 30

1 unit $= \dfrac{30}{3} = 10$

4 units $= 4 \times 10 = 40$

There are 40 buns.

Part-Whole Model (Ratio)

When a whole is divided into a number of parts, a ratio is used to express the relative sizes of the parts. This can be illustrated by the part-whole model, or by the comparison model. For example, the following part-whole model shows that the whole is divided into two parts in the ratio 4 : 3.

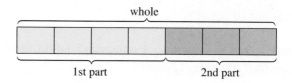

The two parts of the whole can also be represented by the comparison model:

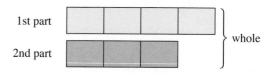

Given the ratio and any of the three quantities: the whole (7 units), first part (4 units) and second part (3 units), students can find the other two quantities using the unitary method.

Example 4 (Primary 5A)

Mary cut a piece of ribbon 30 m long into three pieces in the ratio 3 : 2 : 5. What was the length of the longest piece?

Here the part-whole model shows a whole divided into three parts in the ratio 3 : 2 : 5.

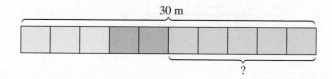

The three parts represent the three pieces of ribbon of length 3 units, 2 units and 5 units respectively.

Alternatively, students may draw the comparison model:

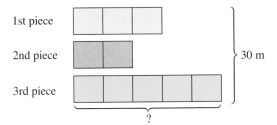

Given the total length (10 units), students can find the length of the longest piece (5 units) using the unitary method:

10 units = 30 m

1 unit $= \dfrac{30}{10} = 3$ m

5 units $= 5 \times 3 = 15$ m

The length of the longest piece was 15 m.

III. Percentage

Part-Whole Model (Percentage)

A part of a whole can be expressed as a fraction, and also as a percentage. When a whole is divided into 100 equal parts, each part is $\dfrac{1}{100}$ of the whole, or 1% of the whole.

The part-whole model can be used to illustrate the concept of percentage. For example,

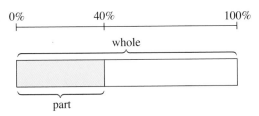

The model shows that the shaded part is 40% of the whole. This is indicated by a percentage scale as shown. In the part-whole model, the whole is taken as the base (100%). If the whole is 100 units, then the shaded part is 40 units. The percentage 40% means 40 units out of 100 units.

Given the whole, students can find a percentage part using the unitary method. For example, if the whole (100%) is 500, students can find 40% of the whole as follows:

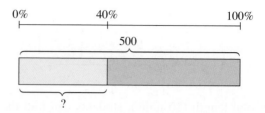

100 units = 500

1 unit $= \dfrac{500}{100} = 5$

40 units $= 40 \times 5 = 200$

40% of 500 is 200.

Conversely, if the percentage part is given, i.e. 40% of the whole is 200, students can find the whole (100%) as follows:

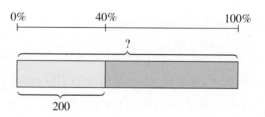

40 units $= 200$

1 unit $= \dfrac{200}{40} = 5$

100 units $= 100 \times 5 = 500$

The whole is 500.

Example 5 (Primary 5B)

There were 500 people at a concert. 30% of them were children. How many children were there at the concert?

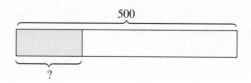

Here a bar is drawn to represent the whole (500 people). The shaded part, which is 30% of the whole, represents the number of children. The percentage 30% means 30 units out of 100 units. Students can find the number of children (30 units) as follows:

$$100 \text{ units} = 500$$
$$1 \text{ unit} \quad = \frac{500}{100} = 5$$
$$30 \text{ units} \quad = 30 \times 5 = 150$$

There were 150 children at the concert.

Comparison Model (Percentage)

The comparison model can be used to compare two quantities by percentage. For example, the following model shows two quantities A and B such that A is 80% of B.

Here B is taken as the base (100%), and A is compared relative to B. The percentage 80% means 80 units to 100 units.

"A is 80% of B" is the same as "A is 20% less than B".

Conversely, if A is taken as the base (100%), and B is compared relative to A, then B is 125% of A (see Notes 4.2, p. 41). The percentage 125% means 125 units to 100 units.

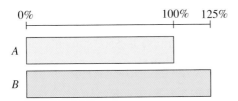

"B is 125% of A" is the same as "B is 25% more than A".

It is important to note that "A is 20% less than B" is not the same as "B is 20% more than A".

Fraction, decimal and percentage are related. For example, 80% means $\frac{80}{100}$ which is the same as $\frac{4}{5}$ or 0.8. Also, 125% means $\frac{125}{100}$ which is the same as $\frac{5}{4}$ or 1.25 (see Notes 4.3, p. 41).

Suppose that B (100 units) is 400, students can find A (80 units):

100 units = 400

1 unit $\quad = \frac{400}{100} = 4$

80 units $\quad = 80 \times 4 = 320$

A is 320.

Conversely, if A (80 units) is given as 320, students can find B (100 units).

Example 6 (Primary 6A)

Ali has $50. Rahmat has 20% more money than Ali. How much money does Rahmat have?

Here the comparison model is used to compare Rahmat's money relative to Ali's money.

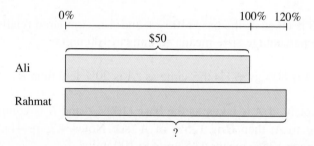

In the model, Ali's money is taken as the base (100%). Rahmat's money is 20% more than Ali's. So Rahmat's money is 120% of Ali's. The percentage 120% means 120 units to 100 units. Given that Ali's money (100 units) is $50, students can find Rahmat's money (120 units) as follows:

100 units = $50

1 unit $\quad = \$ \frac{50}{100} = \$0.50$

120 units $= 120 \times \$0.50 = \$60$

Rahmat has $60.

Example 7 (Primary 6A)

Parcel A weighs 5 kg. Parcel B is 15% lighter than parcel A. Find the mass of parcel B.

The following model shows that the mass of parcel B is 85% of that of parcel A. That is, parcel B is 15% lighter than parcel A.

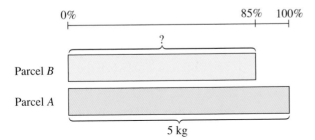

The mass of parcel A is taken as the base (100%). The percentage 85% means 85 units to 100 units. Given that the mass of parcel A (100 units) is 5 kg, students can find the mass of parcel B (85 units) as follows:

100 units = 5 kg

1 unit $= \dfrac{5}{100} = 0.05$ kg

85 units $= 85 \times 0.05 = 4.25$ kg

The mass of parcel B is 4.25 kg.

In Example 7, if the mass of parcel B (85 units) is given as 4.25 kg, students can find the mass of parcel A (100 units) as follows:

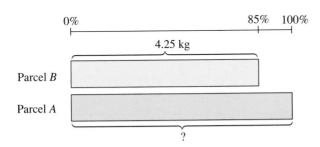

85 units $= 4.25$ kg

1 unit $= \dfrac{4.25}{85} = 0.05$ kg

100 units $= 100 \times 0.05 = 5$ kg

The mass of parcel A is 5 kg.

Notes

4.1 Two quantities can be compared in many ways. For example, the following comparison model shows that there are 4 times as many boys as girls:

Girls
Boys

Difference	The difference between the number of girls and the number of boys is 3 units.
Multiple	The number of boys is 4 times the number of girls.
Fraction	The number of girls is $\frac{1}{4}$ times the number of boys.
Ratio	The ratio of the number of boys to the number of girls is 4 : 1.
	The ratio of the number of girls to the number of boys is 1 : 4.

The following comparison model shows that there are $\frac{3}{5}$ as many boys as girls:

Girls
Boys

Difference	The difference between the number of girls and the number of boys is 2 units.
Fraction	The number of boys is $\frac{3}{5}$ times the number of girls.
	The number of girls is $\frac{5}{3}$ times the number of boys.
Ratio	The ratio of the number of boys to the number of girls is 3 : 5.
	The ratio of the number of girls to the number of boys is 5 : 3.

4.2 If A is 80% of B, then:

$$A = 0.8B \qquad \text{(or} \quad A = \frac{4}{5}B)$$

$$B = \frac{A}{0.8} = 1.25A \qquad \text{(or} \quad B = \frac{5}{4}A)$$

B is 125% of A.

4.3 Percentage, fraction and decimal are related. For example,

Percentage	A is 80% as much as B.	B is 125% as much as A.
	A is 20% less than B.	B is 25% more than A.
Fraction	A is $\frac{4}{5}$ times B.	B is $\frac{5}{4}$ times A.
Decimal	A is 0.8 times B.	B is 1.25 times A.

5

Model Method and Problem Solving

Solving word problems is an important basic skill in mathematics. It reinforces the learning and deepens the understanding of mathematics concepts through application in meaningful contexts.

In this chapter, we demonstrate how the Model Method is used to represent and solve structurally complex word problems. The method entails drawing a pictorial model, and finding the so-called "1 unit" from the model (the unitary method). The model enables students to process the given information, and make sense of the known and unknown quantities and their relationships.

Example 1 (Primary 4B)

48 children went to the zoo. $\frac{3}{8}$ of them were girls. How many boys were there?

Here a bar is drawn to represent the whole (total number of children). It comprises 8 units, of which 3 units are shaded to represent the number of girls ($\frac{3}{8}$ of the whole). The other 5 units represent the number of boys ($\frac{5}{8}$ of the whole).

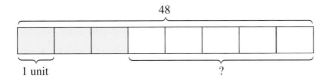

The part-whole model shows that the whole (8 units) is 48. From the model, students find the value of 1 unit, and hence find the number of boys (5 units).

8 units = 48

1 unit $= \dfrac{48}{8} = 6$

5 units $= 5 \times 6 = 30$

There are 30 boys.

Example 2 (Primary 5A)

Peter collected a total of 1170 stamps. He collected 4 times as many Singapore stamps as foreign stamps. How many Singapore stamps did he collect?

Here two bars are drawn to represent the number of Singapore stamps and the number of foreign stamps, which are 4 units and 1 unit respectively.

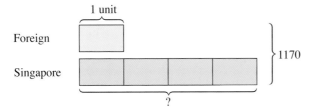

The comparison model shows that the total number of stamps (5 units) is 1170. From the model, students find the value of 1 unit, and hence find the number of Singapore stamps (4 units).

$$5 \text{ units} = 1170$$
$$1 \text{ unit} = \frac{1170}{5} = 234$$
$$4 \text{ units} = 4 \times 234 = 936$$

There were 936 Singapore stamps.

Example 3 (Primary 5A)

Mrs Lin made 300 tarts. She sold $\frac{3}{4}$ of them and gave $\frac{1}{3}$ of the remainder to her neighbour. How many tarts had she left?

Here a bar is drawn to represent the whole (300). $\frac{3}{4}$ of the whole represents the number of tarts sold.

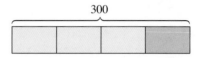

300

The remaining $\frac{1}{4}$ is divided into 3 units. The number of tarts given away is 1 unit, and the number of tarts left is 2 units.

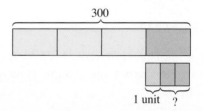

300

1 unit   ?

From the model, students find the value of 1 unit, and hence find the number of tarts left (2 units).

Method 1

$$3 \text{ units} = 300 \div 4 = 75$$
$$1 \text{ unit} = \frac{75}{3} = 25$$
$$2 \text{ units} = 2 \times 25 = 50$$

Mrs Lin had 50 tarts left.

Method 2

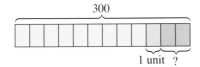

Here the bar is divided into the same units, and the whole is 12 units.

12 units = 300

1 unit $= \dfrac{300}{12} = 25$

2 units $= 2 \times 25 = 50$

Mrs Lin had 50 tarts left.

The Model Method is a *synthetic-analytic* process. When students use the Model Method to solve a problem, they construct a pictorial model to describe and interpret the problem situation, to understand the problem structure, and to process and analyse the given information (the *synthetic* approach). Then they use the model to plan and develop a sequence of logical steps for the solution of the problem (the *analytic* approach). This involves finding the value of 1 unit from the model (the unitary method) as a strategy to work out the solution (Kho, 1987).

Example 4 (Primary 6B)

Meiling spent an equal amount of money each day. After 4 days, she had $\dfrac{4}{5}$ of her money left. After another 10 days, she had $30 left. How much money did she have at first?

Here a bar is drawn to represent the whole (the amount of money Meiling had at first). $\dfrac{4}{5}$ of the whole represents the amount of money left. The remaining $\dfrac{1}{5}$ represents the amount of money spent in 4 days.

After 4 days:

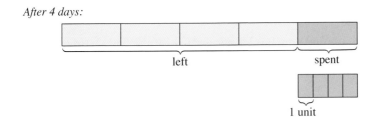

The amount of money spent each day is 1 unit. To solve the problem, the bar is divided into the same units. The amount of money spent after 14 days is 14 units. The amount of money left ($30) is 6 units.

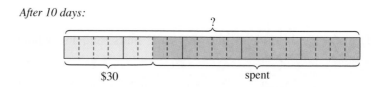

After 10 days:

$30   spent

From the model, students find the value of 1 unit, and hence find the whole amount of money (20 units).

6 units = $30

1 unit   = $$\frac{30}{6}$$ = $5

20 units = 20 × $5 = $100

Meiling had $100 at first.

Example 5 (Primary 6B)

Raju had 3 times as much money as Gopal. After Raju had spent $60 and Gopal had spent $10, they each had an equal amount of money left. How much money did Raju have at first?

This problem involves a *before* situation and an *after* situation. In the *before* situation, Raju had 3 times as much money as Gopal. In the *after* situation, they each had an equal amount of money left.

Two bars are drawn to represent Raju's money and Gopal's money, which are 3 units and 1 unit respectively, in the *before* situation.

Before:

Raju

Gopal

The comparison model shows that Raju had 3 times as much money as Gopal.

In the *after* situation, the comparison model comprises two equal bars which show that Raju and Gopal each had an equal amount of money left. The *before* and *after* situations are connected to show that Raju had spent $60 and Gopal had spent $10.

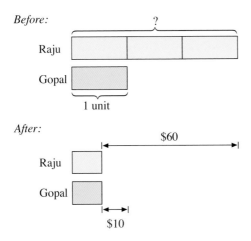

Before:

Raju

Gopal

1 unit

After:

$60

Raju

Gopal

$10

From the model, students find the value of 1 unit, and hence find the amount of money Raju had at first (3 units).

2 units = $60 − $10 = $50

1 unit $= \$\dfrac{50}{2} = \$25$

3 units = 3 × $25 = $75

Raju had $75 at first.

Example 6 (Primary 6B)

$\dfrac{3}{5}$ *of the beads in a box are yellow beads. The rest are red beads and blue beads. There are twice as many yellow beads as red beads. There are 30 more red beads than blue beads. Find the total number of yellow beads and red beads.*

Here a bar is drawn to represent the whole (the total number of beads in the box). $\dfrac{3}{5}$ of the whole represents the number of yellow beads. The remaining $\dfrac{2}{5}$ represents the total number of red beads and blue beads.

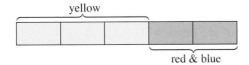

yellow

red & blue

Next, $\frac{2}{5}$ of the whole is sub-divided so that the yellow beads are twice as many as the red beads.

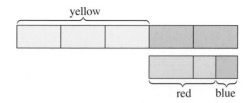

Method 1

Take the number of blue beads as 1 unit. The number of red beads and the number of yellow beads are 3 units and 6 units respectively.

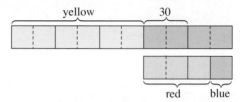

The difference between the number of red beads and the number of blue beads is 2 units. From the model, students find the value of 1 unit, and hence find the total number of yellow beads and red beads (9 units).

$$2 \text{ units} = 30$$
$$1 \text{ unit} \ = \frac{30}{2} = 15$$
$$9 \text{ units} = 9 \times 15 = 135$$

The total number of yellow beads and red beads is 135.

Method 2

Take the number of yellow beads as 3 units. The difference between the number of red beads and the number of blue beads is 1 unit. Here 1 unit is 30.

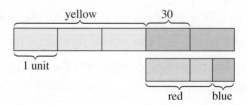

Number of yellow beads = $3 \times 30 = 90$
Number of red beads = $90 \div 2 = 45$
Total number of yellow beads and red beads = $90 + 45 = 135$

Example 7 (Primary 6B)

The ratio of Sumin's money to Meili's money was 4 : 1. After Sumin had spent $26, Sumin had $2 less than Meili. How much money did Sumin have at first?

The following model represents the *before* and *after* situations. In the *before* situation, the ratio of Sumin's money to Meili's money was 4 : 1. In the after situation, Meili's money remained unchanged, and Sumin's money became $2 less than Meili's. The two situations are connected to show that Sumin had spent $26.

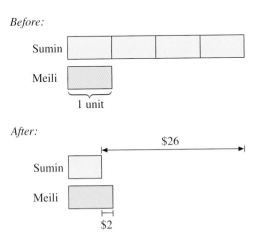

From the model, students find the value of 1 unit, and hence find the amount of money Sumin had at first (4 units).

3 units = $26 − $2 = $24

1 unit $= \$\dfrac{24}{3} = \$8$

4 units = 4 × $8 = $32

Sumin had $32 at first.

Example 8 (Primary 6B)

The ratio of Peter's money to John's money was 3 : 5 at first. After Peter's money was increased by $250 and John's money was decreased by $350, they each had an equal amount of money. How much money did Peter have at first?

49

The following model represents the *before* and *after* situations. In the *before* situation, the ratio of Peter's money to John's money was 3 : 5. In the *after* situation, Peter and John each had an equal amount of money. The two situations are connected to show that Peter's money was increased by $250 and John's money was decreased by $350.

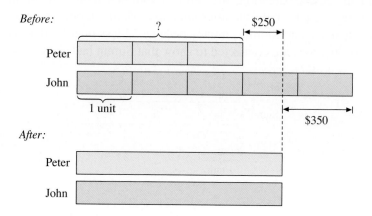

From the model, students find the value of 1 unit, and hence find the amount of money Peter had at first (3 units).

2 units = $250 + $350 = $600

1 unit = $$\frac{600}{2}$ = $300

3 units = 3 × $300 = $900

Peter had $900 at first.

Example 9 (Primary 6B)

Jenny and Marvin have 836 stamps altogether. Jenny has 20% more stamps than Marvin. How many more stamps does Jenny have than Marvin?

The following model shows that the number of Jenny's stamps is 20% more than Marvin's.

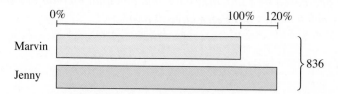

The number of Marvin's stamps is taken as the base (100%). The number of Jenny's stamps is 120% as compared with the number of Marvin's stamps. The number of Marvin's stamps and the number of Jenny's stamps are 100 units and 120 units respectively. The total number of stamps is 220 units. The difference between the two numbers is 20 units. From the model, students find the value of 1 unit, and hence find the difference (20 units).

Method 1

220 units = 836

1 unit $= \dfrac{836}{220} = 3.8$

20 units $= 20 \times 3.8 = 76$

Jenny has 76 more stamps than Marvin.

Method 2

220 units = 836

20 units $= \dfrac{836}{220} \times 20 = 76$

Jenny has 76 more stamps than Marvin.

Method 3

220% $\longrightarrow$ 836

20% $\longrightarrow \dfrac{836}{220} \times 20 = 76$

Jenny has 76 more stamps than Marvin.

This example will be shown again in the next chapter (Example 5, p. 63), where we discuss how the Model Method can be integrated with the algebraic method to solve problems.

6

Model Method and Algebra

In Singapore, students in secondary school are required to use the algebraic method to solve problems. The algebraic method entails the formulation and solution of algebraic equations in the process of solving problems. It is well known that students often have difficulty in formulating algebraic equations to represent the information given in word problems (Stacey and MacGregor, 2000). Many of them also have difficulty solving the equations because of weak algebraic manipulation skills. As students are familiar with using the Model Method to solve word problems, they would continue to use the Model Method if they are not competent in the algebraic method. Indeed the Model Method can be integrated with the algebraic method for solving algebra word problems (Kho, 1987, 2005, 2007; Fong, 1994; Ng, 2001; Cheong, 2002; Beckmann, 2004). An article regarding this approach has been published in *Teaching Secondary School Mathematics: A Resource Book* (Kho, 2007) and is reproduced in Appendix C on page 115.

In Chapter 5, we have discussed how the Model Method is used to solve word problems without using the algebraic method. In this chapter, the Model Method is integrated with the algebraic method to help students develop their competence and confidence in using the algebraic method.

Integration of the Model Method and Algebra

The following examples illustrate how the Model Method can be integrated with the algebraic method in solving algebra word problems.

Example 1

There are 50 children in a dance group. If there are 10 more boys than girls, how many girls are there?

The algebraic method involves using a letter symbol such as x to represent an unknown quantity. For example, let x be the number of girls. As there are 10 more boys than girls, the number of boys is $x + 10$. The total number of boys and girls is $x + (x + 10)$, which is equal to 50. Thus students obtain the following equation to solve the problem:

$$x + (x + 10) = 50$$

The solution of the equation is $x = 20$.

There are 20 girls.

Students can draw the comparison model to represent the problem situation, and use it to solve the problem using the unitary method or the algebraic method.

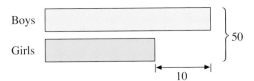

This model shows that the total number of boys and girls is 50, and that the difference between the number of boys and the number of girls is 10.

Unitary method

Take the number of girls as 1 unit. Students find the value of 1 unit and solve the problem as follows:

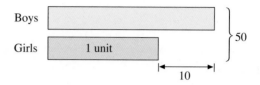

2 units = 50 − 10 = 40
1 unit = 40 ÷ 2 = 20

There are 20 girls.

Algebraic method

Let x be the number of girls.

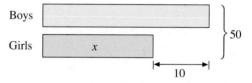

The model enables students to express the number of boys in terms of x as shown in the following two variations.

Variation 1

The number of boys is 10 more than the number of girls. It is expressed as $x + 10$.

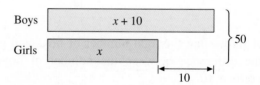

From the model, students see that the sum of $(x + 10)$ and x is 50, so they obtain the equation:

$$(x + 10) + x = 50$$

The solution of the equation is $x = 20$.

There are 20 girls.

Variation 2

The total number of boys and girls is 50. The number of boys can be expressed as $50 - x$.

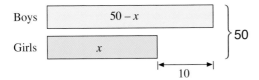

From the model, students see that the difference between $(50 - x)$ and x is 10, so they obtain the equation:

$$(50 - x) - x = 10$$

The solution of the equation is $x = 20$.

There are 20 girls.

As the number of boys and the number of girls are both unknown quantities, students may instead let x be the number of boys, and express the number of girls in terms of x. They will obtain a different equation to solve the problem. The following are alternative solutions to the problem.

Variation 3

The number of girls is $x - 10$.

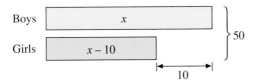

From the model, students obtain the equation:

$$x + (x - 10) = 50$$

The solution of the equation is $x = 30$.

$$x - 10 = 20$$

There are 20 girls.

The number of girls is $50 - x$.

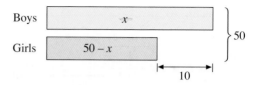

From the model, students obtain the equation:

$$x - (50 - x) = 10$$

The solution of the equation is $x = 30$.

$$x - 10 = 20$$

There are 20 girls.

Example 2

A has 3 times as much money as B.
B has \$200 less than C.
C has \$50 more than A.
Find the total amount of money that A, B and C have.

The problem can be solved using the unitary method as follows:

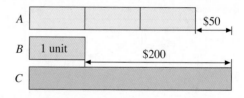

2 units = \$200 − \$50 = \$150
1 unit = \$150 ÷ 2 = \$75

A's money = 3 units = 3 × \$75 = \$225
B's money = \$75
C's money = \$225 + \$50 = \$275

Total amount of money = \$225 + \$75 + \$275 = \$575

In this problem, it is impractical to let x be the total amount of money. This will make the algebraic method very difficult. As there are three unknown quantities: *A*'s, *B*'s and *C*'s money, students may let x be any of these, and then express the other two in terms of x (see Notes 6.1, p. 64).

For example, let x be B's money:

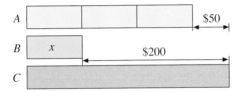

Variation 1

A's money is $3x$, and C's money is $3x + 50$.

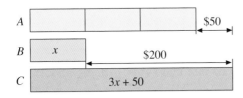

From the model, students obtain the equation:

$3x + 50 = x + 200$

The solution of the equation is $x = 75$.

$3x + x + (3x + 50) = 7x + 50 = 575$

The total amount of money is $575.

Variation 2

A's money is $3x$, and C's money is $x + 200$.

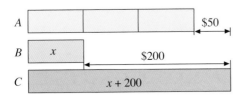

From the model, students obtain the equation:

$3x + 50 = x + 200$

The solution of the equation is $x = 75$.

$3x + x + (x + 200) = 5x + 200 = 575$

The total amount of money is $575.

From the model, students may see that $2x + 50 = 200$, which gives $x = 75$.

The Model Method is a means, not an end in itself. It helps students formulate an algebraic equation to solve the problem. While the more able students can proceed quickly to the abstract algebraic method to solve problems without drawing a model, others may still need to rely on drawing the model as a problem-solving heuristic. Students may draw an incomplete model when they solve problems by the algebraic method, as illustrated by the next example.

Example 3

Mary spent $\dfrac{3}{5}$ of her money on a dictionary. She spent another $\dfrac{1}{3}$ of her money on a pen. She spent \$84 altogether. How much money did she have at first?

The following model shows the amount of money spent on the dictionary and the amount of money spent on the pen respectively.

Dictionary

Pen

Variation 1

Let x be Mary's money at first.

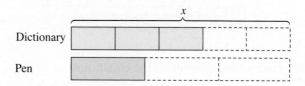

From the model, students obtain the equation:

$$\frac{3}{5}x + \frac{1}{3}x = 84$$

The solution of the equation is $x = 90$.

Mary spent \$90 altogether.

<u>Variation 2</u>

Let $5x$ be Mary's money at first. The amount of money spent on the dictionary and the amount of money spent on the pen are $3x$ and $\frac{5x}{3}$ respectively.

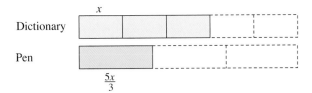

From the model, students obtain the equation:

$$3x + \frac{5x}{3} = 84$$

The solution of the equation is $x = 18$.

$$5x = 90$$

Mary spent $90 altogether.

Example 4

It is given that the number of fifty-cent coins and twenty-cent coins are in the ratio 2 : 3. If 4 of the fifty-cent coins are exchanged for twenty-cent coins, the ratio will become 2 : 7. What is the total value ($) of the set of coins?

The following model represents the *before* and *after* situations of the problem.

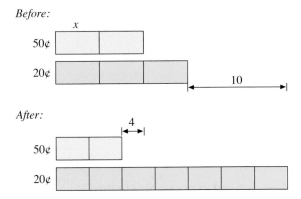

The model shows that the number of 50¢ coins decreases by 4, and the number of 20¢ coins increases by 10. In the *before* situation, the ratio of the number of 50¢ coins to that of 20¢ coins is 2 : 3. In the *after* situation, the ratio is 2 : 7.

<u>Variation 1</u>

Let $2x$ and $7x$ be the number of 50¢ coins and the number of 20¢ coins respectively, in the *after* situation.

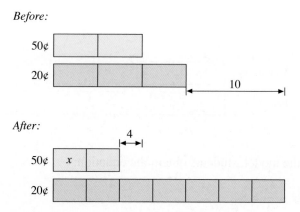

The number of 50¢ coins and the number of 20¢ coins in the *before* situation are $2x + 4$ and $7x - 10$ respectively.

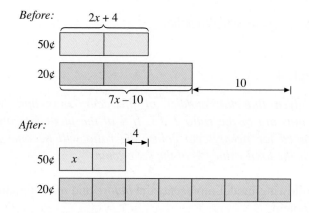

From the model, students see that the ratio of $2x + 4$ to $7x - 10$ is $2 : 3$. Thus they obtain the equation:

$$\frac{2x + 4}{7x - 10} = \frac{2}{3}$$

As both $\dfrac{2x + 4}{2}$ and $\dfrac{7x - 10}{3}$ are equal to 1 unit, students may write the equation as:

$$\frac{2x + 4}{2} = \frac{7x - 10}{3}$$

In either case, the equation can be rewritten as

$3(2x + 4) = 2(7x - 10)$, or as $2x + 4 = \dfrac{2}{3}(7x - 10)$.

The solution is $x = 4$.

$$0.5(2x) + 0.2(7x) = 2.4x = 9.6$$

The total value is \$9.60.

60

Variation 2

Students may see that 1 unit in the *before* situation is $x + 2$. Thus the number of 50¢ coins and the number of 20¢ coins in the *before* situation are $2(x + 2)$ and $3(x + 2)$ respectively.

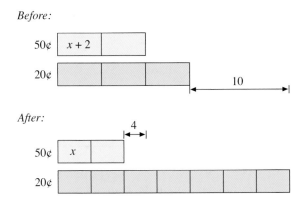

From the model, students obtain the equation:

$$7x - 3(x + 2) = 10$$

The solution of the equation is $x = 4$.

$$0.5(2x) + 0.2(7x) = 2.4x = 9.6$$

The total value is $9.60.

Variation 3

Let $2x$ and $3x$ be the number of 50¢ coins and the number of 20¢ coins respectively, in the before situation.

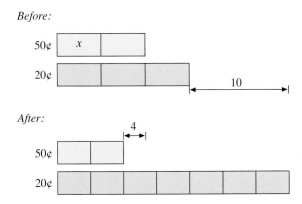

The number of 50¢ coins and the number of 20¢ coins in the *after* situation are $2x - 4$ and $3x + 10$ respectively.

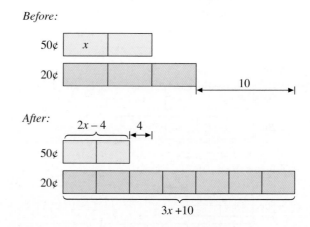

From the model, students obtain the equation:

$$\frac{2x - 4}{3x + 10} = \frac{2}{7} \qquad \text{(or} \quad \frac{2x - 4}{2} = \frac{3x + 10}{7})$$

The equation can be rewritten as $7(2x - 4) = 2(3x + 10)$, or as $2x - 4 = \frac{2}{7}(3x + 10)$. The solution is $x = 6$.

$$0.5(2x) + 0.2(3x) = 1.6x = 9.6$$

The total value is \$9.60.

Variation 4

Students may obtain an algebraic equation from either the *before* or the *after* situation. For example, in the *before* situation, the numbers of 50¢ coins and 20¢ coins are $2x$ and $3x$ respectively.

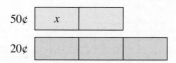

With the model, students can figure out the equation:

$$\frac{2x - 4}{3x + 10} = \frac{2}{7}$$

The solution of the equation is $x = 6$.

$$0.5(2x) + 0.2(3x) = 1.6x = 9.6$$

The total value is \$9.60.

Example 5

Jenny and Marvin have 836 stamps altogether. Jenny has 20% more stamps than Marvin. How many more stamps does Jenny have than Marvin?

This is Example 9 in Chapter 5. The following model shows that the number of Jenny's stamps is 20% more than Marvin's.

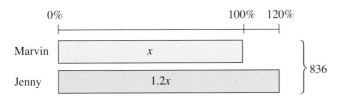

Let x be the number of Marvin's stamps. Then the number of Jenny's stamps is 120% of x. This is $1.2x$. From the model, students obtain the equation:

$$x + 1.2x = 836$$

The solution of the equation is $x = 380$.

$$1.2x - x = 0.2x = 76$$

Jenny has 76 more stamps than Marvin.

When students draw a model and construct an algebraic equation to solve a problem, they can make sense of the use of a letter symbol such as x to represent an unknown quantity, and the formulation of an equation to find the value of x. The Model Method enables students to analyse the information given in the problem, and to conceptualise and formulate an algebraic equation to solve the problem. It is a powerful problem-solving heuristic and empowers students to solve problems, including challenging problems, as illustrated in Appendix D on page 131.

Currently the Singapore Ministry of Education is revamping the teaching of the algebraic method by integrating it with the Model Method. This is intended to help students in the transition from the Model Method to the important and yet abstract algebraic method. An algebra project, led by Dr Kho Tek Hong, was embarked in 2006 to develop a new pedagogy and support resources for algebra. These include the design and development of a software application tool, *AlgeTools*, to support student learning, and the training of teachers on the new approach. The project is near completion and will be reported separately (Looi, Ng & Kho, 2007; Yeo, Thong & Kho, 2008; Yen, Yeo, Thong & Kho, 2008).

Notes

6.1 There are three quantities involved: A's money, B's money and C's money. Students may let x be any of these, and then express the other two in terms of x.

<u>Case 1</u>

Let x be A's money.

Method 1	Method 2
A x	A $x = 3(x - 150)$
B $\dfrac{x}{3}$	B $x - 150$
C $\dfrac{x}{3} + 200 = x + 50$	C $x + 50$

<u>Case 2</u>

Let x be B's money.

Method 3	Method 4
A $3x = x + 150$	A $3x$
B x	B x
C $x + 200$	C $x + 200 = 3x + 50$

<u>Case 3</u>

Let x be C's money.

Method 5	Method 6
A $x - 50$	A $x - 50 = 3(x - 200)$
B $x - 200 = \dfrac{x - 50}{3}$	B $x - 200$
C x	C x

7

Conclusions

Mathematical problem solving is the focus of the Singapore Mathematics Framework. Students learn to solve not only basic word problems, but also non-routine, open-ended and real-world problems. In this monograph, we deal with basic word problems only. These problems facilitate the acquisition and application of basic mathematics concepts and skills, and the development of mathematical thinking.

In the preceding chapters, we have discussed the use of the Model Method for effective mathematics learning and problem solving. The method is an important feature of the Singapore primary mathematics curriculum, and it serves to develop and enhance students' mathematical thinking and problem-solving abilities in the early years of mathematics education. In this concluding chapter, some perspectives of problem solving are discussed. These provide the basis that the Model Method is an effective problem-solving strategy. The connection between the Model Method and the algebraic method is also discussed.

Problem-Solving Perspectives

Representations in Problem Solving

A word problem comprises a problem situation, data (quantities and quantitative relationships), and a question. Solving the problem is to find an answer to the question. Students need to understand the problem situation, as well as the relationships between the known and unknown quantities (the *problem comprehension* process) before they work out the answer to the question (*solution*).

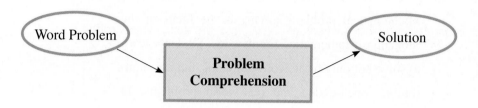

Problem representation plays an important role in the problem comprehension process. For example, in the algebraic method, students formulate an algebraic equation to represent the problem situation and to connect the known and unknown quantities. Then they solve the equation to work out the answer to the question.

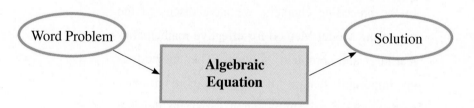

When students use the Model Method in conjunction with the algebraic method, they construct a pictorial model to help them formulate an algebraic equation to solve the problem.

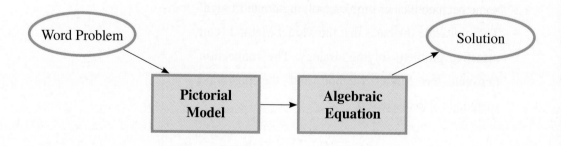

Schemas in Problem Solving

In the cognitive theory of learning, schemas (or schemata) are building blocks of mental structures and cognitive processes. Students construct schemas in the process of learning and problem solving. They use the schemas to successfully comprehend and solve problems. For example, the part-whole model and the comparison model are pictorial forms of Greeno's part-part-whole and comparison schemas for addition and subtraction word problems (Greeno, 1978: Nesher, Greeno, & Riley, 1982). These schemas represent the conceptual structures of word problems. The pictorial representations enable students to visualise the problem structure and make sense of the quantitative relationships involved in a problem. The various problem structures given in Appendix B can also be regarded as problem schemas. When students solve a problem using the Model Method, they consciously make use of an appropriate problem schema to construct a model, fit in the data given in the problem, and plan for the solution based on the model. The method allows students to conceptualise the mathematics concepts and processes, and this develops their competence and confidence in solving word problems. Also, students can integrate the learning of the algebraic method with the Model Method. In this way, they build new schemas for the algebraic method from the schemas for the Model Method.

Metacognition in Problem Solving

Effective problem solving involves both cognitive and metacognitive processes. Research findings have shown that metacognition, and self-regulation of learning in particular, enhances students' problem-solving abilities. Students should learn not only mathematics knowledge and heuristics, but also how to monitor and self-regulate their problem-solving processes (Schoenfeld, 1985, 1987).

The Singapore mathematics curriculum has adopted Polya's four-step problem-solving process since 1990 (see Notes 7.1, p. 69). These include:

1. Understanding the problem
2. Devising a plan
3. Carrying out the plan
4. Looking back

(Polya, 1945)

The Model Method facilitates Polya's problem-solving process:

Step 1: Students construct a model to represent a problem. The model helps them understand the problem situation and the quantitative relationships involved.

Step 2: The model enables students to devise a plan to solve the problem. For a one-step word problem, the model helps students decide what operation to use to solve the problem. For a two-step or multi-step word problem, the model helps them identify the intermediate step(s), or formulate a sequence of steps to solve the problem. In the algebraic method, students use the model to help them formulate an algebraic equation to solve the problem.

Step 3: Students carry out arithmetic calculations, or solve the algebraic equation, in order to answer the question given in the problem.

Step 4: Students evaluate and check if the answer satisfies the data given in the problem, or if the answer is reasonable. Besides checking the calculation and the formulation of the algebraic equation, they may re-look and examine the construction of the model, if necessary.

The fourth step enables students to acquire and develop metacognitive skills. They may modify and improve their solutions by repeating the earlier steps. They are also encouraged to think of other methods to solve the same problem, and to extend the same method to some other problems.

Model Method And Algebraic Method

The use of the part-whole and comparison models as pictorial representations facilitates meaningful learning of the abstract concepts of the four operations, fraction, ratio and percentage in the early years of mathematics education. It also helps students, especially the visual learners, develop their competence and confidence in solving the related word problems. When students use the Model Method to solve a problem, they draw a pictorial model as a visual representation of the quantities (known and unknown) and their relationships given in the problem. The model enhances their thinking and problem-solving skills. Many students are able to solve complex word problems. They are also able to use the model to help them articulate and communicate their thinking and solution, and thus engage themselves in active and collaborative learning.

The Model Method is a pre-algebraic method. In Singapore, students use the Model Method before they learn to solve algebraic equations. Their experience in using bars to represent quantities in the Model Method would enable them to appreciate better the use of letter symbols to represent quantities when they later learn the algebraic method (Kho, 1987). To solve a problem, students may start with drawing a pictorial model. Instead of using the model to work out the arithmetic steps for the solution (the unitary method), they formulate an algebraic equation from the model to solve the problem. The approach provides an enriching opportunity for students to engage in the construction and interpretation of algebraic equations through meaningful and active learning. This will enhance the learning of basic algebra which is a key to mathematics success.

Notes

7.1 Polya's model for problem solving was included in the 1990 Mathematics Syllabus as shown below.

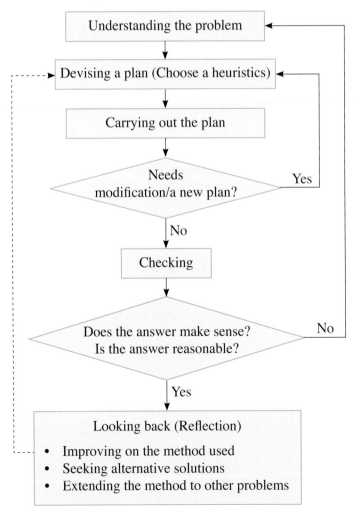

The processes involved in Polya's model were elaborated upon in the 2001 Mathematics Syllabus as shown below.

Steps For Problem Solving

1. Understanding the Problem

    - Look for information given
    - Visualise the information
    - Organise the information
    - Connect the information

2. Devising a Plan
    (Choosing a Heuristic)

    - Act it out
    - Use a diagram/model
    - Use guess and check
    - Make a systematic list
    - Look for pattern(s)
    - Work backwards
    - Use before-after concept
    - Make suppositions
    - Restate the problem in another way
    - Simplify the problem
    - Solve part of the problem
    - Think of a related problem
    - Use equations

3. Carrying out the Plan

    - Use computational skills
    - Use geometry skills
    - Use logical reasoning

4. Reflecting

    - Checking solution
    - Improving on the method used
    - Seeking alternative solutions
    - Extending the method to other problems

References

American Institute for Research (AIR, 2005). *What the United States can learn from Singapore's world-class mathematics system (and what Singapore can learn from the United States): An exploratory study.* Washington, DC: Author.

Ang, W. H. (2008). Singapore's textbook experience 1965-97: Meeting the needs of curriculum change. In S. K. Lee, C. B. Goh, B. Fredriksen, & J. P. Tan (Eds.), *Toward a better future: Education and training for economic development in Singapore since 1965* (pp. 69–95). Washington, DC: World Bank.

Beckmann, S. (2004). Solving algebra and other story problems with simple diagrams: A method demonstrated in grade 4–6 texts used in Singapore. *The Mathematics Educator, 14*(1), 42–46.

Cheong, N. P. (2002). The teaching of primary mathematics and the model approach to problem solving. *Mathematics Newsletter* (Issue No. 4, 2002), Ministry of Education, Singapore.

Curriculum Development Institute of Singapore (CDIS, 1987). *A report on Primary Mathematics Project (Jul 1980–Dec 1987).* Singapore: Author.

Department of Education and Science. (1982). *Mathematics counts: The Cockcroft report of the committee of enquiry into the teaching of mathematics in schools.* London: HMSO.

Fong, H. K. (1994). Bridging the gap between secondary and primary mathematics. *Teaching and Learning, 14*(2), 73–84.

Goh, C. B. & Gopinathan, S. (2008). The development of education in Singapore since 1965. In S. K. Lee, C. B. Goh, B. Fredriksen, & J. P. Tan (Eds.), *Toward a better future: Education and training for economic development in Singapore since 1965* (pp. 12–38). Washington, DC: World Bank.

Greeno, J. G. (1978). A study of problem solving. In R. Glaser (Ed.), *Advances in instructional psychology (Vol. 1).* Hillsdale, NJ: Lawrence Erbaum Associates.

Kho, T. H. (1987). Mathematical models for solving arithmetic problems. *Proceedings of the 4th Southeast Asian Conference on Mathematics Education (ICMI-SEAMS)* (pp. 345–351). Singapore.

Kho, T. H. (1989). Teaching thinking in mathematics. *Proceedings of the Seminar on Trends in Science Education* (pp. 54–59). Singapore.

Kho, T. H. (2005). The model-drawing method with algebra. In *Making sense of algebra* (pp. 1–14). Singapore: Ministry of Education.

Kho, T. H. (2007). The model-drawing method with algebra. In P. Y. Lee (Ed.), *Teaching secondary school mathematics: A resource book* (pp. 393–412). Singapore: McGraw-Hill.

Looi, C. K., Ng, F. K., & Kho, T. H. (2007). *Technology-enabled pedagogy to bridge bar diagrams to letter symbolic algebra.* Paper presented at the 15th International Conference on Computers in Education, Hiroshima, Japan.

Ministry of Education (MOE, 1979). *Report on the Ministry of Education 1978* (by Dr Goh and his team). Singapore: Author.

Ministry of Education (MOE, 1981). *Diagnostic tests on the basic skills of mathematics for primary school pupils.* Singapore: Author.

Ministry of Education (MOE, 1990). *Mathematics syllabus (Primary).* Singapore: Author.

Ministry of Education (MOE, 2000). *Mathematics syllabus (Primary).* Singapore: Author.

Ministry of Education (MOE, 2006). *Mathematics syllabus (Primary).* Singapore: Author.

National Council of Teachers of Mathematics (NCTM, 1980). *An agenda for action: Recommendations for school mathematics of the 1980s.* Reston, VA: Author.

National Research Council. (2001). *Adding it up: Helping children learn mathematics.* J. Kilpatrick, J. Swafford, & B. Findell (Eds.), Mathematics Learning Study Committee, Center for Education, Division of Behavioral and Social Sciences and Education. Washington, DC: National Academies Press.

Nesher, P., Greeno, J. G., & Riley, M. S. (1982). The development of semantic categories for addition and subtraction. *Educational Studies in Mathematics, 13*(4), 373–394.

Ng, S. F. (2001). Secondary school students' perceptions of the relationship between the model method and algebra. *Proceedings of the 12th International Congress of Mathematical Instruction (ICMI) Study Conference* (pp. 468–474). Melbourne, Australia.

Polya, G. (1945). *How to solve it: A new aspect of mathematical method.* Princeton, NJ: Princeton University Press.

RAND Mathematics Study Panel. (2003). *Mathematical proficiency of all students: Toward a strategic research and development program in mathematics education.* Santa Monica, CA: RAND Corporation.

Schoenfeld, A. H. (1985). *Mathematical problem solving.* San Diego, CA: Academic Press.

Schoenfeld, A. H. (1987). What's all the fuss about metacognition? In A. H. Schoenfeld (Ed.), *Cognitive science and mathematics education* (pp. 189–215). Hillsdale, NJ: Lawrence Erlbaum Associates, Publishers.

Soh, C. K. (2005). *An overview of mathematics education in Singapore.* Paper presented at the 1st International Mathematics Curriculum Conference, Chicago, USA.

Soh, C. K. (2008). An overview of mathematics education in Singapore. In Z. Usiskin, & E. Willmore (Eds.), *Mathematics curriculum in Pacific Rim countries: China, Japan, Korea, and Singapore: Proceedings of a conference* (pp. 23–36). Charlotte, NC: Information Age.

Stacey, K., & MacGregor, M. (2000). Learning the algebraic method of solving problems. *Journal of Mathematical Behavior, 18*(2), 149–167.

Wong, K. Y. (2002). Helping your students to become metacognitive in mathematics: A decade later. *Mathematics Newsletter* (Issue No. 4, Apr 2002). Singapore: Ministry of Education.

Yen, Y. P., Yeo, S. M., Thong, C. H., & Kho, T. H. (2008). *An ICT-rich pedagogy for quadratic expansion and factorisation.* Paper presented at the International Conference on Teaching and Learning with Technology, Singapore.

Yeo, S. M., Thong, C. H., & Kho, T. H. (2008). *Algebra discs: Digital manipulatives for learning algebra.* Paper presented at the 11th International Congress on Mathematics Education, Monterrey, Mexico.

Yip, S. K., & Sim, W. K. (Eds.). (1990). *Evolution of educational excellence: 25 years of education in the Republic of Singapore.* Singapore: Longman.

Mathematical Models for Solving Arithmetic Problems

(Reproduced from the *Proceedings of the Fourth Southeast Asian Conference on Mathematics Education* 1987, pp. 345–351)

Introduction

One way to enhance students' ability in solving problems is to help them visualise abstract mathematical relationships and various problem structures through pictorial representations. In this article, the use of mathematical models in the form of pictorial representations is discussed. Examples are given to show how the models can be used to solve various problems. The main features are:

(a) The model method helps students gain a better insight into mathematical concepts such as fraction, ratio and percentage.

(b) The model method helps students plan the solution steps for solving an arithmetic word problem.

(c) The model method is comparable to, but is less abstract than the algebraic method.

(d) The model method can motivate students to solve challenging problems.

Mathematical Models

The Part-Whole Model

The part-whole model (also known as the 'part-part-whole' model) shows the various parts which make up a whole, e.g.

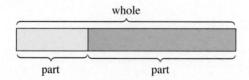

Here the whole is divided into two parts. When the two parts are given, we can find the whole by addition. When the whole and one part are known, we can find the other part by subtraction.

Example 1

Minah goes shopping. She buys a handbag for $120 and is left with $168. How much money does she have at first?

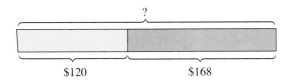

We draw a bar to represent the amount of money Minah has at first. It is marked with a question mark (?) to indicate that the amount is unknown. As shown in the model, both parts are known, so we find the whole by addition:

$120 + $168 = $288

Minah has $288 at first.

In the part-whole model, the whole may be divided into more than two parts. We can find the whole by multiplying one part by the number of parts, when all the parts are equal, e.g.

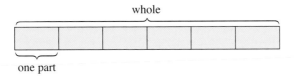

Conversely, given the whole, we can find one part or the number of parts by division.

The Comparison Model

The comparison model shows the relationship between two quantities when they are compared. We may compare two quantities by showing their difference, e.g.

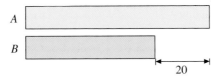

A is 20 more than *B*; or *B* is 20 less than *A*. In other words, the difference between *A* and *B* is 20.

We may also compare two quantities by showing their ratio, e.g.

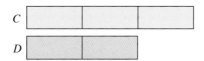

C is $\dfrac{3}{2}$ of D; or D is $\dfrac{2}{3}$ of C. In other words, the ratio of C to D is 2 : 3.

When two quantities are given, we can find the difference or ratio. Conversely, when one quantity and the difference or ratio are given, we can find the other quantity.

The Change Model

The change model shows the relationship between the new value of a quantity and its original value after an increase or a decrease, e.g.

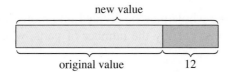

The increase is 12.

The increase or decrease may be expressed as a fraction of the original value, e.g.

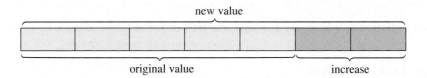

The increase is $\dfrac{2}{5}$ of the original value.

The increase or decrease may also be expressed as a percentage of the original value, e.g.

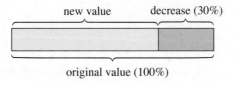

The decrease is 30% of the original value.

Knowing the increase or decrease, we can find the new value from the original value and vice-versa.

Problems Involving Fraction, Ratio and Percentage

The use of models will help students understand and solve arithmetic word problems. When dealing with problems involving fraction, ratio and percentage, it will also help students gain a better insight into the various mathematical concepts.

In the following examples, the model method as well as the usual method for solving problems are presented. The usual method is abstract and if this is the only method taught, many students will have difficulty in solving problems. They will resort to learning by rote. On the other hand, the model method makes use of a pictorial model to illustrate the concept of fraction, ratio and percentage. The solution steps are explicit. Therefore if the model method is taught prior to the usual method, it will help students understand the usual method.

Example 2

Minah had 20 m of cloth. She used $\frac{3}{5}$ of it to make some dresses for her dolls. How many metres of cloth did she use?

The model method

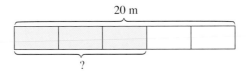

We use the part-whole model to show $\frac{3}{5}$ of 20 m. Here the whole is divided into 5 equal parts of which 3 parts are shaded. In other words, the whole comprises 5 units, so $\frac{3}{5}$ of it comprises 3 units. We have:

    5 units = 20 m
    1 unit = 20 ÷ 5 = 4 m
    3 units = 3 × 4 = 12 m

    She used 12 m of cloth.

The usual method

    Amount of cloth used = $\frac{3}{5}$ × 20 = 12 m

Example 3

Devi and Minah shared a prize money of $420 in the ratio 4 : 3. How much money did Devi receive?

The model method

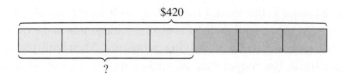

Suppose the whole comprises 7 units, then the ratio 4 : 3 means Devi received 4 units and Minah received 3 units. We have:

7 units = $420
1 unit = $420 ÷ 7 = $60

Minah's share = 4 units = 4 × $60 = $240

The usual method

Minah's share = $\frac{4}{7}$ × $420 $\doteq$ $240

Example 4

A book contains 200 pages. 35% of the pages are in colour. How many pages are in colour?

The model method

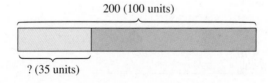

Suppose the whole comprises 100 units, then 35% of it comprises 35 units. We have:

100 units = 200
1 unit   = 200 ÷ 100 = 2
35 units = 35 × 2 = 70

70 pages are in colour.

$$\text{Number of pages in colour} = 35\% \times 200 = \frac{35}{100} \times 200 = 70$$

The Model Method and the Algebraic Method

Without the models, students may have to resort to the algebraic method to solve structurally complex problems. The model method is less abstract than the algebraic method and can be introduced before students learn to solve algebraic equations. Indeed the models serve as good pictorial representations of algebraic equations. If students are taught the model method first, when they eventually learn the algebraic method, they will appreciate better the use of symbols to represent quantities as they have experienced using bars to represent quantities in the model method.

Example 5

Devi is 10 kg heavier than Minah. Their total mass is 100 kg. Find Devi's mass.

The model method

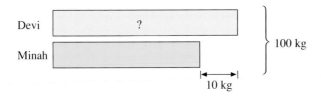

We use the comparison model to show the relationship between Devi's mass and Minah's mass. Suppose Minah's mass is 1 unit, then Devi's mass is 1 unit and 10 kg as shown.

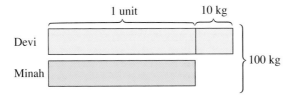

The total mass is 2 units + 10 kg. We have:

2 units = 100 − 10 = 90 kg
1 unit = 90 ÷ 2 = 45 kg

Devi's mass = 45 + 10 = 55 kg

The algebraic method

Let Minah's mass be x kg, then Devi's mass is $(x + 10)$ kg. We have:

Total mass $= x + (x + 10) = (2x + 10)$ kg

Hence, $2x + 10 = 100$
$$2x = 90$$
$$x = 45$$

Devi's mass $= x + 10 = 45 + 10 = 55$ kg

Challenging Problems

The following examples show how the model method can motivate students to solve challenging problems in an elementary and interesting manner. The method has been established as a generalised method for solving arithmetic word problems. It is a *synthetic-analytic* process. First, we construct a model to help us describe and interpret the problem situation and understand the problem structure by processing the given information (the *synthetic* approach). Then we use the model to help us develop a sequence of logical steps for the solution of the problem (the *analytic* approach). The model reveals the hidden information and helps us relate unknown and known quantities. It is a powerful tool for solving complex problems.

Example 6

Devi and Minah have $520 altogether. If Devi spends $\frac{2}{5}$ of her money and Minah spends $40, then they will have the same amount of money left. How much money does Devi have?

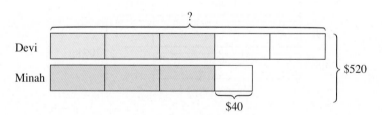

Here we use the comparison model in combination with the change model. The shaded parts show that the two remaining amounts of money are equal (i.e. 3 units each). The total amount of money is 8 units + $40. We have:

8 units $= \$520 - \$40 = \$480$
1 unit $\ = \$480 \div 8 = \$60$

Devi's money $= 5$ units $= 5 \times \$60 = \$300$

Example 7

Devi's salary and Minah's salary are in the ratio 4 : 5. If Devi's salary is increased by 30%, by what percentage must Minah's salary be increased or decreased so that they will have the same salary?

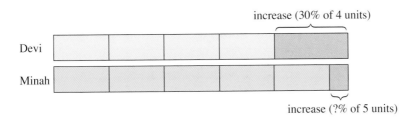

increase (30% of 4 units)

Devi

Minah

increase (?% of 5 units)

The model shows that Devi's salary is 4 units and Minah's salary is 5 units at first. It also shows that their new salaries are equal. We have:

Increase in Devi's salary = 30% × 4 units = 1.2 units

Increase in Minah's salary = 1.2 units – 1 unit = 0.2 unit

Percentage increase = $\frac{0.2}{5} \times 100\% = 4\%$

Conclusion

The model method was introduced in Singapore at the Primary Four level in 1983. Teachers are encouraged to use the method in their classrooms. Generally, the method is well received, and teachers are able to assign structurally complex problems as challenging problems to the more able students. By doing so, the students will be more receptive to unfamiliar problems and their problem-solving ability will be enhanced. However, it will take several years for all teachers to be acquainted with this method and teach it in their classrooms. In the meantime, some studies can be carried out in the classrooms to determine the effectiveness of the method and to improve the instruction of the method.

Problem Structures of Basic Word Problems

Type 1: Part-Whole Model (Addition and Subtraction)

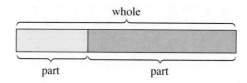

A whole divided into two parts.

<u>Variations:</u>

1. Given two parts.
   To find the whole.

   134 girls and 119 boys took part in an art competition. How many children took part in the competition?

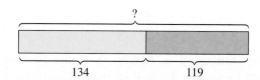

   134 + 119 = 253

   253 children took part in the art competition.

2. Given the whole and a part.
   To find the other part.

   253 children took part in an art competition. If there were 134 boys, how many girls were there?

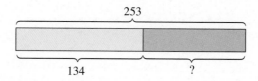

   253 − 134 = 119

   There were 119 girls.

Type 2: Comparison Model (Addition and Subtraction)

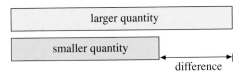

Two quantities and their difference.

<u>Variations:</u>

1. Given two quantities.

    (a) To find the difference.

    Meilin saved $184 and Betty saved $121. How much less than Meilin did Betty save?

    Meilin | $184

    Betty | $121 | ?

    184 – 121 = 63

    Betty saved $63 less than Meilin.

    (b) To find the sum.

    Meilin saved $184 and Betty saved $121. How much did they save altogether?

    Meilin | $184

    Betty | $121 | ?

    184 + 121 = 305

    They saved $305 altogether.

2. Given the larger quantity and the difference.
To find the smaller quantity.

Meilin saved $184. Betty saved $63 less than Meilin. How much did Betty save?

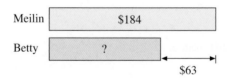

184 − 63 = 121

Betty saved $121.

3. Given the smaller quantity and the difference.
To find the larger quantity.

Betty saved $121. She saved $63 less than Meilin. How much did Meilin save?

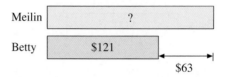

121 + 63 = 184

Meilin saved $184.

4. Given one quantity and the sum.
To find the other quantity.

Meilin and Betty saved $305 altogether. Meilin saved $184. How much did Betty save?

Meilin $184

Betty ?

$305

305 − 184 = 121

Betty saved $121.

Meilin and Betty saved $305 altogether. Betty saved $121. How much did Meilin save?

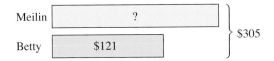

$305 - 121 = 184$

Meilin saved $184.

Type 3: Part-Whole Model (Multiplication and Division)

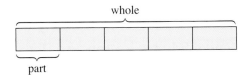

A whole divided into a number of equal parts.

<u>Variations:</u>

1. Given the number of parts and one part.
    To find the whole.

    5 children shared the cost of a present equally. Each of them paid $6. What was the cost of the present?

    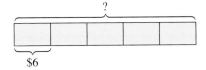

    $5 \times 6 = 30$

    The cost of the present was $30.

2. Given the whole and the number of parts.
    To find one part.

    5 children bought a present for $30. They shared the cost equally. How much did each child pay?

    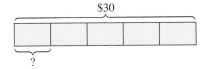

    $30 \div 5 = 6$

    Each child paid $6.

3.   Given the whole and one part.
     To find the number of parts.

A group of children bought a present for $30. They paid $6 each. How many children were there in the group?

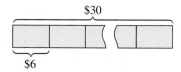

$30 \div 6 = 5$

There were 5 children in the group.

Type 4: Comparison Model (Multiplication and Division)

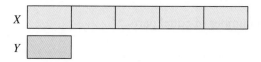

A quantity as a multiple of another quantity, e.g. X is 5 times as much as Y.

<u>Variations:</u>

1.   Given the smaller quantity and the multiple.
     To find the larger quantity.

A farmer has 7 ducks. He has 5 times as many chickens as ducks. How many chickens does he have?

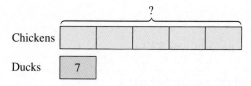

$5 \times 7 = 35$

He has 35 chickens.

2. Given the larger quantity and the multiple.
   To find the smaller quantity.

   A farmer has 35 chickens. He has 5 times as many chickens as ducks. How many ducks does he have?

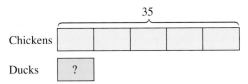

   $35 \div 5 = 7$

   He has 7 ducks.

3. Given the smaller quantity and the multiple.

   (a) To find the difference.

   A farmer has 7 ducks. He has 5 times as many chickens as ducks. How many more chickens than ducks does he have?

   $4 \times 7 = 28$

   He has 28 more chickens than ducks.

   (b) To find the sum.

   A farmer has 7 ducks. He has 5 times as many chickens as ducks. How many chickens and ducks does he have altogether?

   $6 \times 7 = 42$

   He has 42 chickens and ducks altogether.

4. Given the difference and the multiple.
   To find the smaller quantity.

   A farmer has 28 more chickens than ducks. He has 5 times as many chickens as ducks. How many ducks does he have?

   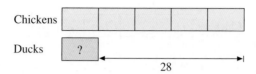

   $28 \div 4 = 7$

   He has 7 ducks.

5. Given the sum and the multiple.
   To find the smaller quantity.

   A farmer has a total of 42 chickens and ducks. He has 5 times as many chickens as ducks. How many ducks does he have?

   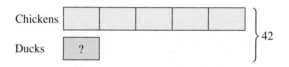

   $42 \div 6 = 7$

   He has 7 ducks.

6. Given two quantities.
   To find the multiple.

   A farmer has 7 ducks and 35 chickens. How many times as many chickens as ducks does he have?

   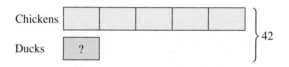

   $35 \div 7 = 5$

   He has 5 times as many chickens as ducks.

Type 5: Comparison Model and 2-Step Word Problems

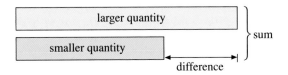

Two quantities and their sum and difference.

Variations:

1. Given the larger quantity and the difference.
   To find the sum.

   Meilin saved $184. Betty saved $63 less than Meilin. How much did they save altogether?

   Meilin | $184
   Betty | | $63 | }?

   $184 - 63 = 121$
   $184 + 121 = 305$

   They saved $305 altogether.

2. Given the smaller quantity and the difference.
   To find the sum.

   Betty saved $121. She saved $63 less than Meilin. How much did they save altogether?

   Meilin | |
   Betty | $121 | $63 | }?

   $121 + 63 = 184$
   $184 + 121 = 305$

   They saved $305 altogether.

3. Given one quantity and the sum.
   To find the difference.

   Meilin and Betty saved $305 altogether. If Meilin saved $184, how much less than Meilin did Betty save?

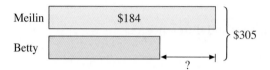

   305 − 184 = 121
   184 − 121 = 63

Betty saved $63 less than Meilin.

   Meilin and Betty saved $305 altogether. If Betty saved $121, how much less than Meilin did Betty save?

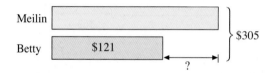

   305 − 121 = 184
   184 − 121 = 63

   Betty saved $63 less than Meilin.

4. Given the sum and difference.

   (a) To find the smaller quantity.

   Meilin and Betty saved $305 altogether. Betty saved $63 less than Meilin. How much did Betty save?

Meilin
Betty ?
$63
$305

   305 − 63 = 242
   242 ÷ 2 = 121

   Betty saved $121.

(b) To find the larger quantity.

Meilin and Betty saved $305 altogether. Betty saved $63 less than Meilin. How much did Meilin save?

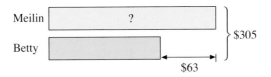

$305 + 63 = 368$
$368 \div 2 = 184$

Meilin saved $184.

5. Given the larger quantity and the multiple.

(a) To find the difference.

A farmer has 35 chickens. He has 5 times as many chickens as ducks. How many more chickens than ducks does he have?

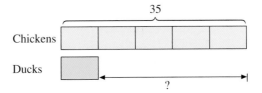

$35 \div 5 = 7$
$4 \times 7 = 28$

He has 28 more chickens than ducks.

(b) To find the sum.

A farmer has 35 chickens. He has 5 times as many chickens as ducks. How many chickens and ducks does he have altogether?

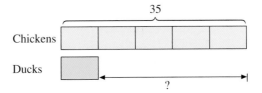

$35 \div 5 = 7$
$6 \times 7 = 42$

He has 42 chickens and ducks altogether.

6. Given the difference and the multiple.

(a) To find the larger quantity.

A farmer has 28 more chickens than ducks. He has 5 times as many chickens as ducks. How many chickens does he have?

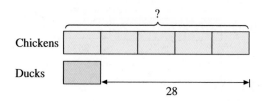

28 ÷ 4 = 7
5 × 7 = 35

He has 35 chickens.

(b) To find the sum.

A farmer has 5 times as many chickens as ducks. He has 28 more chickens than ducks. How many chickens and ducks does he have altogether?

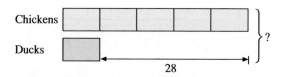

28 ÷ 4 = 7
6 × 7 = 42

He has 42 chickens and ducks altogether.

7. Given the sum and the multiple.

(a) To find the larger quantity.

A farmer has a total of 42 chickens and ducks. He has 5 times as many chickens as ducks. How many chickens does he have?

42 ÷ 6 = 7
5 × 7 = 35

He has 35 chickens.

(b) To find the difference.

A farmer has a total of 42 chickens and ducks. He has 5 times as many chickens as ducks. How many more chickens than ducks does he have?

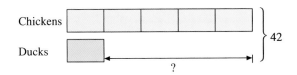

$42 \div 6 = 7$
$4 \times 7 = 28$

He has 28 more chickens than ducks.

Type 6: Part-Whole Model (Fraction)

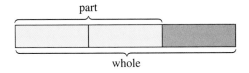

A part as a fraction of the whole, e.g. the part is $\frac{2}{3}$ of the whole.

<u>Variations:</u>

1. Given the whole and the fraction.

    (a) To find the part related to the fraction.

    Salmah bought 24 flowers. $\frac{2}{3}$ of them were white. How many white flowers were there?

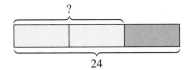

    3 units = 24
    1 unit = 24 ÷ 3 = 8
    2 units = 2 × 8 = 16

    There were 16 white flowers.

(b) To find the other part.

Salmah bought 24 flowers. $\frac{2}{3}$ of them were white. How many flowers were not white?

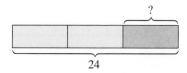

3 units = 24
1 unit = 24 ÷ 3 = 8

8 flowers were not white.

2. Given a part and the related fraction.

(a) To find the whole.

Salmah bought some flowers. $\frac{2}{3}$ of them were white. If there were 16 white flowers, how many flowers did Salmah buy?

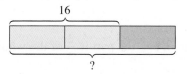

2 units = 16
1 unit = 16 ÷ 2 = 8
3 units = 3 × 8 = 24

Salmah bought 24 white flowers.

(b) To find the other part.

Salmah bought some flowers. $\frac{2}{3}$ of them were white. If there were 16 white flowers, how many flowers were not white?

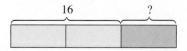

2 units = 16
1 unit = 16 ÷ 2 = 8

8 flowers were not white.

Type 7: Comparison Model (Fraction)

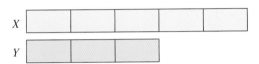

A quantity as a fraction of another quantity, e.g. Y is $\frac{3}{5}$ as much as X, or X is $\frac{5}{3}$ as much as Y.

<u>Variations:</u>

1. Given one of the quantities and the fraction.

    (a) To find the other quantity.

        There are $\frac{3}{5}$ as many boys as girls. If there are 75 girls, how many boys are there?

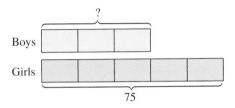

    5 units = 75
    1 unit = 75 ÷ 5 = 15
    3 units = 3 × 15 = 45

    There are 45 boys.

    There are $\frac{3}{5}$ as many boys as girls. If there are 45 boys, how many girls are there?

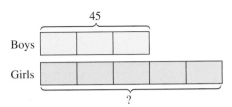

    3 units = 45
    1 unit = 45 ÷ 3 = 15
    5 units = 5 × 15 = 75

    There are 75 girls.

95

(b) To find the sum.

There are $\frac{3}{5}$ as many boys as girls. If there are 75 girls, how many children are there altogether?

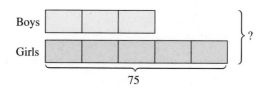

5 units = 75
1 unit = 75 ÷ 5 = 15
8 units = 8 × 15 = 120

There are 120 children altogether.

There are $\frac{3}{5}$ as many boys as girls. If there are 45 boys, how many children are there altogether?

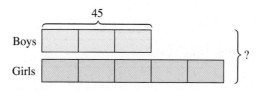

3 units = 45
1 unit = 45 ÷ 3 = 15
8 units = 8 × 15 = 120

There are 120 children altogether.

(c) To find the difference.

There are $\frac{3}{5}$ as many boys as girls. If there are 75 girls, how many more girls than boys are there?

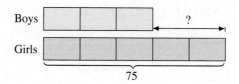

5 units = 75
1 unit = 75 ÷ 5 = 15
2 units = 2 × 15 = 30

There are 30 more girls than boys.

There are $\frac{3}{5}$ as many boys as girls. If there are 45 boys, how many more girls than boys are there?

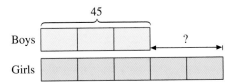

3 units = 45
1 unit = 45 ÷ 3 = 15
2 units = 2 × 15 = 30

There are 30 more girls than boys.

2.   Given the sum and the fraction.

(a)   To find one of the quantities.

There are $\frac{3}{5}$ as many boys as girls. If there are 120 children altogether, how many girls are there?

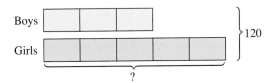

8 units = 120
1 unit = 120 ÷ 8 = 15
5 units = 5 × 15 = 75

There are 75 girls.

There are $\frac{3}{5}$ as many boys as girls. If there are 120 children altogether, how many boys are there?

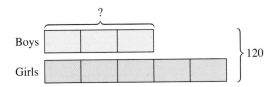

8 units = 120
1 unit = 120 ÷ 8 = 15
3 units = 3 × 15 = 45

There are 45 boys.

(b) To find the difference.

There are $\frac{3}{5}$ as many boys as girls. If there are 120 children altogether, how many more girls than boys are there?

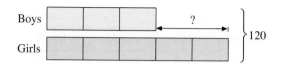

8 units = 120
1 unit = 120 ÷ 8 = 15
2 units = 2 × 15 = 30

There are 30 more girls than boys.

3. Given the difference and the fraction.

(a) To find one of the quantities.

There are $\frac{3}{5}$ as many boys as girls. If there are 30 more girls than boys, how many girls are there?

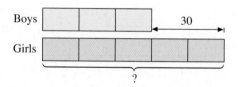

2 units = 30
1 unit = 30 ÷ 2 = 15
5 units = 5 × 15 = 75

There are 75 girls.

There are $\frac{3}{5}$ as many boys as girls. If there are 30 more girls than boys, how many boys are there?

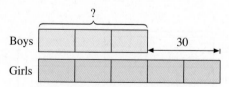

2 units = 30
1 unit = 30 ÷ 2 = 15
3 units = 3 × 15 = 45

There are 45 boys.

(b)   To find the sum.

There are $\frac{3}{5}$ as many boys as girls. If there are 30 more girls than boys, how many children are there altogether?

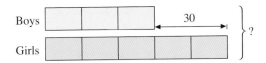

2 units = 30
1 unit = 30 ÷ 2 = 15
8 units = 8 × 15 = 120

There are 120 children altogether.

Type 8: Part-Whole Model (Ratio)

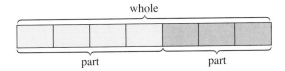

A whole divided into two or three parts in a given ratio, e.g. the whole is divided into two parts in the ratio 4 : 3.

<u>Variations:</u>

1.   Given the whole and the ratio.
     To find one of the parts.

Siti and Mary shared $35 in the ratio 4 : 3. How much money did Siti receive?

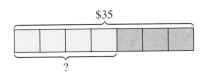

7 units = $35
1 unit = $35 ÷ 7 = $5
4 units = 4 × $5 = $20

Siti received $20.

Mary cut a piece of ribbon 30 m long into 3 pieces in the ratio 3 : 2 : 5. What was the length of the longest piece?

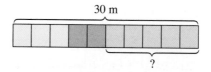

10 units = 30 m
1 unit = 30 ÷ 10 = 3 m
5 units = 5 × 3 = 15 m

The length of the longest piece of ribbon was 15 m.

2. Given one part and the ratio.

(a) To find the whole.

Siti and Mary shared a sum of money in the ratio 4 : 3. Siti received $20. How much money did they share?

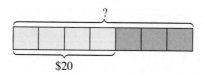

4 units = $20
1 unit = $20 ÷ 4 = $5
7 units = 7 × $5 = $35

They shared $35.

Mary cut a piece of ribbon into 3 pieces in the ratio 3 : 2 : 5. If the longest piece was 15 m, what was the original length of the ribbon?

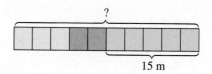

5 units = 15 m
1 unit = 15 ÷ 5 = 3 m
10 units = 10 × 3 = 30 m

The original length of the ribbon was 30 m.

(b) To find another part.

Siti and Mary shared a sum of money in the ratio 4 : 3. Siti received $20. How much money did Mary receive?

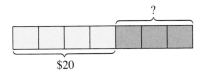

4 units = $20
1 unit = $20 ÷ 4 = $5
3 units = 3 × $5 = $15

Mary received $15.

Mary cut a piece of ribbon into 3 pieces in the ratio 3 : 2 : 5. If the longest piece was 15 m, how long was the shortest piece?

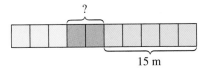

5 units = 15 m
1 unit = 15 ÷ 5 = 3 m
2 units = 2 × 3 = 6 m

The shortest piece of ribbon was 6 m long.

Type 9: Comparison Model (Ratio)

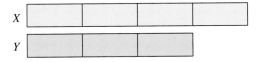

Two or three quantities related by a ratio, e.g. the ratio of X to Y is 4 : 3, or the ratio of Y to X is 3 : 4.

<u>Variations:</u>

1. Given one of the quantities and the ratio.

    (a) To find another quantity.

The ratio of the mass of parcel X to that of parcel Y is 5 : 3. If parcel X weighs 40 kg, what is the mass of parcel Y?

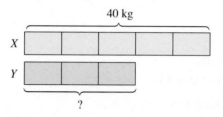

5 units = 40 kg
1 unit = 40 ÷ 5 = 8 kg
3 units = 3 × 8 = 24 kg

The mass of parcel *Y* is 24 kg.

The ratio of the number of pies to the number of cakes to the number of buns is 3 : 1 : 4. If there are 30 pies, how many buns are there?

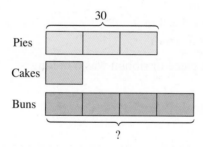

3 units = 30
1 unit = 30 ÷ 3 = 10
4 units = 4 × 10 = 40

There are 40 buns.

(b) To find the sum.

The ratio of the mass of parcel X to that of parcel Y is 5 : 3. If parcel X weighs 40 kg, what is the total mass of the two parcels?

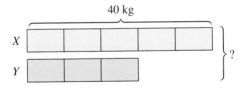

5 units = 40 kg
1 unit = 40 ÷ 5 = 8 kg
8 units = 8 × 8 = 64 kg

The total mass of the two parcels is 64 kg.

The ratio of the number of pies to the number of cakes to the number of buns is 3 : 1 : 4. If there are 30 pies, what is the total number of pies, cakes and buns?

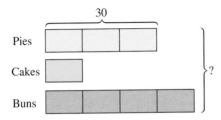

3 units = 30
1 unit = 30 ÷ 3 = 10
8 units = 8 × 10 = 80

The total number is 80.

(c) To find the difference.

The ratio of the mass of parcel X to that of parcel Y is 5 : 3. If parcel X weighs 40 kg, how much is parcel X heavier than parcel Y?

40 kg

X

Y
?

5 units = 40 kg
1 unit = 40 ÷ 5 = 8 kg
2 units = 2 × 8 = 16 kg

Parcel *X* is 16 kg heavier than parcel *Y*.

The ratio of the number of pies to the number of cakes to the number of buns is 3 : 1 : 4. If there are 40 buns, how many more buns than cakes are there?

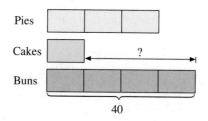

4 units = 40
1 unit = 40 ÷ 4 = 10
3 units = 3 × 10 = 30

There are 30 more buns than cakes.

2. Given the sum and the ratio.

(a) To find one of the quantities.

The ratio of the mass of parcel X to that of parcel Y is 5 : 3. If they weigh 64 kg altogether, what is the mass of parcel X?

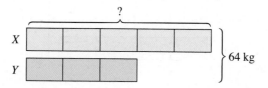

8 units = 64 kg
1 unit = 64 ÷ 8 = 8 kg
5 units = 5 × 8 = 40 kg

The mass of parcel X is 40 kg.

The ratio of the number of pies to the number of cakes to the number of buns is 3 : 1 : 4. If the total number of pies, cakes and buns is 80, how many buns are there?

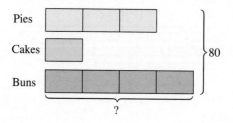

8 units = 80
1 unit = 80 ÷ 8 = 10
4 units = 4 × 10 = 40

There are 40 buns.

(b) To find the difference.

The ratio of the mass of parcel X to that of parcel Y is 5 : 3. If they weigh 64 kg altogether, how much is parcel X heavier than parcel Y?

X [ ][ ][ ][ ][ ] ⎫
                  ⎬ 64 kg
Y [ ][ ][ ] ←—?—→ ⎭

8 units = 64 kg
1 unit = 64 ÷ 8 = 8 kg
2 units = 2 × 8 = 16 kg

Parcel *X* is 16 kg heavier than parcel *Y*.

The ratio of the number of pies to the number of cakes to the number of buns is 3 : 1 : 4. If the total number of pies, cakes and buns is 80, how many more buns than cakes are there?

Pies [ ][ ][ ]   ⎫
Cakes [ ] ←—?—→   ⎬ 80
Buns [ ][ ][ ][ ]   ⎭

8 units = 80
1 unit = 80 ÷ 8 = 10
3 units = 3 × 10 = 30

There are 30 more buns than cakes.

3. Given the difference between two quantities and the ratio.

(a) To find one of the quantities.

The ratio of the mass of parcel X to that of parcel Y is 5 : 3. If parcel X is 16 kg heavier than parcel Y, what is the mass of parcel X?

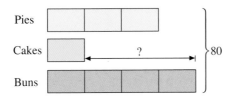

2 units = 16 kg
1 unit = 16 ÷ 2 = 8 kg
5 units = 5 × 8 = 40 kg

The mass of parcel *X* is 40 kg.

The ratio of the number of pies to the number of cakes to the number of buns is 3 : 1 : 4. If there are 30 more buns than cakes, how many buns are there?

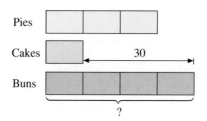

3 units = 30
1 unit = 30 ÷ 3 = 10
4 units = 4 × 10 = 40

There are 40 buns.

(b)   To find the sum.

The ratio of the mass of parcel X to that of parcel Y is 5 : 3. If parcel X weighs 16 kg more than Y, what is the total mass of the parcels?

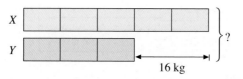

2 units = 16 kg
1 unit = 16 ÷ 2 = 8 kg
8 units = 8 × 8 = 64 kg

The total mass of the parcels is 64 kg.

The ratio of the number of pies to the number of cakes to the number of buns is 3 : 1 : 4. If there are 30 more buns than cakes, what is the total number of pies, cakes and buns?

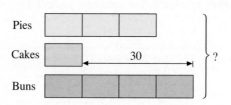

3 units = 30
1 unit = 30 ÷ 3 = 10
8 units = 8 × 10 = 80

The total number is 80.

Type 10: Part-Whole Model (Percentage)

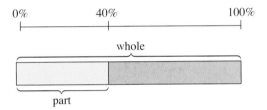

A part as a percentage of the whole, e.g. the part is 40% of the whole.

Variations:

1. Given the whole and the percentage.

   (a) To find the part related to the percentage.

   There were 500 people at a concert. 30% of them were children. How many children were at the concert?

   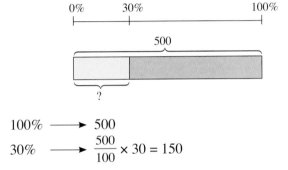

   $$100\% \longrightarrow 500$$
   $$30\% \longrightarrow \frac{500}{100} \times 30 = 150$$

   There were 150 children at the concert.

   (b) To find the other part.

   There were 500 people at a concert. 30% of them were children. How many people at the concert were not children?

   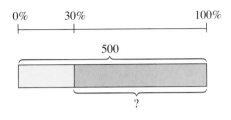

   $$100\% \longrightarrow 500$$
   $$30\% \longrightarrow \frac{500}{100} \times 30 = 150$$

   $$500 - 150 = 350$$

   350 people at the concert were not children.

2. Given a part and the related percentage.

(a) To find the whole.

   30% of the people at a concert were children. If there were 150 children, how many people were at the concert?

   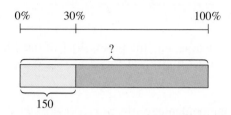

   $$30\% \longrightarrow 150$$
   $$100\% \longrightarrow \frac{150}{30} \times 100 = 500$$

   There were 500 people at the concert.

(b) To find the other part.

   30% of the people at a concert were children. If there were 150 children, how many people at the concert were not children?

   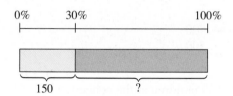

   $$100\% - 30\% = 70\%$$
   $$30\% \longrightarrow 150$$
   $$70\% \longrightarrow \frac{150}{30} \times 70 = 350$$

   350 people at the concert were not children.

Type 11: Comparison Model (Percentage)

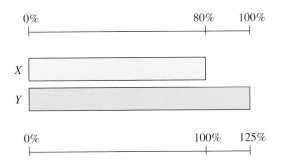

A quantity as a percentage of another quantity, e.g. *X* is 80% of *Y*, or *Y* is 125% of *X*.

Variations:

1. Given one of the quantities and the percentage.

   (a) To find the other quantity.

   Rahmat has 20% more money than Ali. If Ali has \$50, how much money does Rahmat have?

   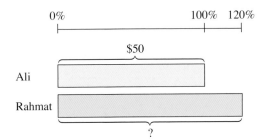

   100% ⟶ \$50

   120% ⟶ $\frac{50}{100} \times 120 = \$60$

   Rahmat has \$60.

Rahmat has 20% more money than Ali. If Rahmat has $60, how much money does Ali have?

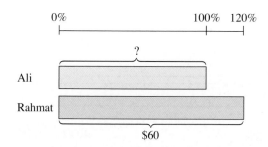

$$120\% \longrightarrow \$60$$

$$100\% \longrightarrow \frac{60}{120} \times 100 = \$50$$

Ali has $50.

(b) To find the difference.

Ali has $50. Rahmat has 20% more money than Ali. How much more money than Ali does Rahmat have?

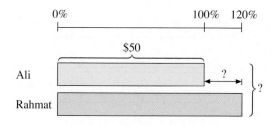

$$100\% \longrightarrow \$50$$

$$20\% \longrightarrow \frac{50}{100} \times 20 = \$10$$

Rahmat has $10 more than Ali.

(c) To find the sum.

Ali has $50. Rahmat has 20% more money than Ali. How much money do they have altogether?

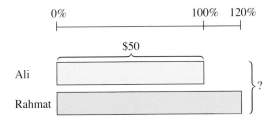

100% ⟶ $50

120% ⟶ $\frac{50}{100} \times 120 = \$60$

$50 + $60 = $110

They have $110 altogether.

2. Given the difference and the percentage.

(a) To find one of the quantities.

Rahmat has 20% more money than Ali. If Rahmat has $10 more than Ali, how much money does Ali have?

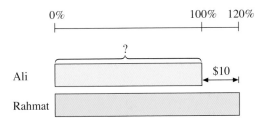

20% ⟶ $10

100% ⟶ $\frac{10}{20} \times 100 = \$50$

Ali has $50.

Rahmat has 20% more money than Ali. If Rahmat has $10 more than Ali, how much money does Rahmat have?

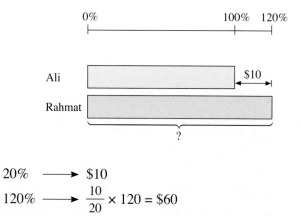

20%   ⟶ $10

120%   ⟶ $\frac{10}{20} \times 120 = \$60$

Rahmat has $60.

(b)   To find the sum.

Rahmat has 20% more money than Ali. If Rahmat has $10 more than Ali, how much money do they have altogether?

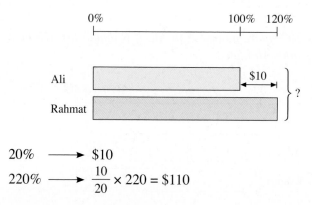

20%   ⟶ $10

220%   ⟶ $\frac{10}{20} \times 220 = \$110$

They have $110 altogether.

3. Given the sum and the percentage.

   (a) To find one of the quantities.

   Rahmat has 20% more money than Ali. If they have $110 altogether, how much money does Ali have?

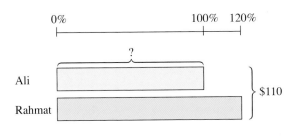

$$220\% \longrightarrow \$110$$
$$100\% \longrightarrow \frac{110}{220} \times 100 = \$50$$

   Ali has $50.

   Rahmat has 20% more money than Ali. If they have $110 altogether, how much money does Rahmat have?

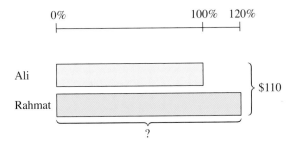

$$220\% \longrightarrow \$110$$
$$120\% \longrightarrow \frac{110}{220} \times 120 = \$60$$

   Rahmat has $60.

(b) To find the difference.

Rahmat has 20% more money than Ali. If they have $110 altogether, how much more money than Ali does Rahmat have?

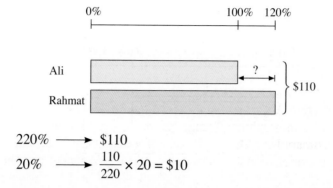

$$220\% \longrightarrow \$110$$

$$20\% \longrightarrow \frac{110}{220} \times 20 = \$10$$

Rahmat has $10 more than Ali.

The Model-Drawing Method with Algebra

(Reproduced from *Teaching Secondary School Mathematics: A Resource Book* 2007, pp. 393–412)

Introduction

One of the main objectives of mathematics education in Singapore is to enable students to develop their abilities in problem solving. The model-drawing method was introduced in the 1980s by the Primary Mathematics Project of the Ministry of Education. It involves the construction of pictorial models, namely the part-whole model and the comparison model, to help students visualise abstract mathematical relationships and various problem structures through pictorial representations (Kho, 1987). It is a powerful visual aid for solving complex problems involving fraction, ratio and percentage. Above all, it is closely related to the algebraic method for solving algebra word problems (Kho, 1987; Fong, 1994; Ng, 2001; Cheong, 2002; Beckmann, 2004).

This article demonstrates how the model-drawing method can help students visualise and conceptualise a problem so that they can formulate an algebraic equation to solve it.

Mathematical Models

The Part-Whole Model

The part-whole model (also known as the 'part-part-whole' model) shows the relationship between a whole and its parts, e.g.

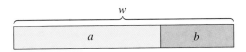

The pictorial model shows that the whole w is divided into two parts a and b. That is, $w = a + b$.

In the part-whole model, we may divide the whole into a number of equal parts, e.g.

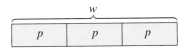

The pictorial model shows that the whole w is divided into 3 equal parts, and each part is p. That is, $w = 3p$.

The Comparison Model

The comparison model shows the relationship between two quantities when they are compared, e.g.

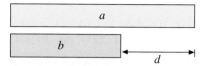

The pictorial model shows that the quantity a is more than the quantity b, and their difference is d. That is, $d = a - b$.

Also,

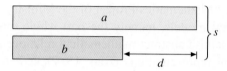

The sum of a and b is s. That is, $s = a + b$.

In the comparison model, we may express one quantity as a multiple of the other, e.g.

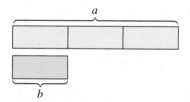

The pictorial model shows that the quantity a is 3 times as much as the quantity b. That is, $a = 3b$.

Example 1

There are 50 children in a dance group. If there are 10 more boys than girls, how many girls are there?

<u>Method 1</u>

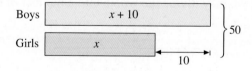

Let the number of girls be x. We form the equation:

$$x + (x + 10) = 50$$

The solution is $x = 20$.

There are 20 girls.

The same problem can be solved by formulating a different equation as shown in the alternative method below:

Method 2

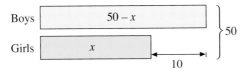

Here we form the equation:

$$(50 - x) - x = 10$$

The solution is $x = 20$.

There are 20 girls.

Example 2

$120 is shared among 3 persons A, B and C. If A receives $20 less than B, and B receives 3 times as much money as C, how much money does C receive?

Method 1

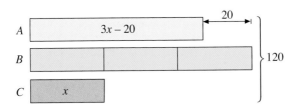

Let C receive $\$x$. We form the equation:

$$(3x - 20) + 3x + x = 120$$

The solution is $x = 20$.

C receives $20.

Method 2

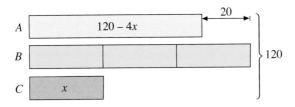

Here we form the equation:

$$3x - (120 - 4x) = 20$$

The solution is $x = 20$.

C receives $20.

Example 3

A has 3 times as much money as B.
B has $200 less than C.
C has $50 more than A.
Find the total amount of money that A, B and C have.

Method 1

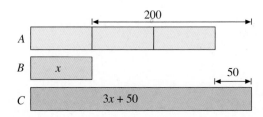

Let B have $\$x$. We form the equation:

$$(3x + 50) - x = 200$$

The solution is $x = 75$.

Total amount of money $= \$(3x + x + 3x + 50) = \$575$

Method 2

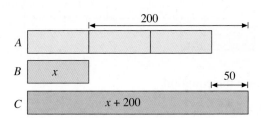

Here we form the equation:

$$(x + 200) - 3x = 50$$

The solution is $x = 75$.

Total amount of money $= \$(3x + x + x + 200) = \$575$

<u>Method 3</u>

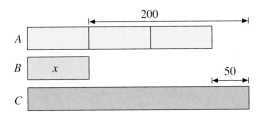

Here we form the equation:

$2x + 50 = 200$

The solution is $x = 75$.

Total amount of money $= \$(3x + x + x + 200) = \$575$

More examples are given as follows.

Example 4

John is 4 times as old as his son. If their total age 10 years ago was 60, find their present ages.   [16, 64]

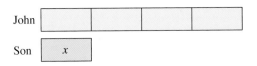

10 years ago:

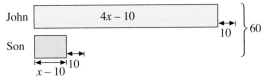

$[(4x - 10) + (x - 10) = 60]$

Example 5

Raju had 3 times as much money as Gopal. After spending $60 each, Raju had 4 times as much money as Gopal. How much money did Raju have at first? [$540]

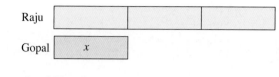

After spending $60 each:

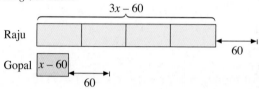

$$[3x - 60 = 4(x - 60)]$$

Example 6

A box contains a total of 200 blue, yellow and orange beads.
Twice the number of blue beads is 10 more than the number of yellow beads.
There are 50 more yellow beads than orange beads.
How many blue beads are there? [54]

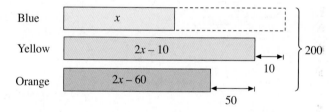

$$[x + (2x - 10) + (2x - 60) = 200]$$

Fraction, Ratio and Percentage

The Part-Whole Model for Fraction

In the part-whole model, when we divide the whole into equal parts, we may use some of the parts to represent a fraction of the whole, e.g.

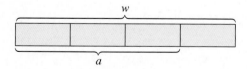

The pictorial model shows that a is $\dfrac{3}{4}$ of w.

In this case, w comprises 4 units, and a is equal to 3 units.

We write: $a = \dfrac{3}{4} w = \dfrac{3w}{4}$

For example, the following model shows $\dfrac{3}{4}$ of a whole.

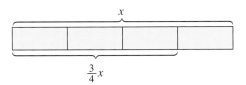

If we let $\dfrac{3}{4}$ of the whole be x, then the whole is $4(\dfrac{x}{3})$.

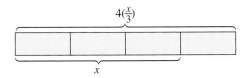

If we let the whole be $4x$, then $\dfrac{3}{4}$ of the whole is $3x$.

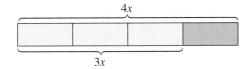

The Comparison Model for Fraction and Ratio

In the comparison model, we may express one quantity as a fraction of the other, e.g.

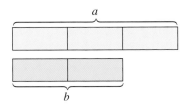

The pictorial model shows that two quantities a and b are 3 units and 2 units respectively.

We say:

a is $\dfrac{3}{2}$ of b.

b is $\dfrac{2}{3}$ of a.

We write:

$a = \dfrac{3}{2}b = \dfrac{3b}{2}$

$b = \dfrac{2}{3}a = \dfrac{2a}{3}$

The relationship between a and b can also be expressed as a ratio.

We say: We write:

The ratio of a to b is 3 : 2. $\dfrac{a}{b} = \dfrac{3}{2}$

The ratio of b to a is 2 : 3. $\dfrac{b}{a} = \dfrac{2}{3}$

For example, the following model shows that one quantity is $\dfrac{2}{3}$ of the other.

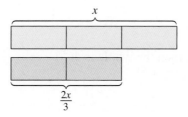

The same model shows that one quantity is $\dfrac{3}{2}$ of the other.

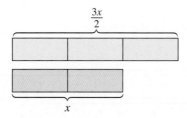

The same model shows that the two quantities are in the ratio 3 : 2.

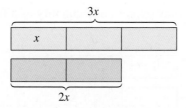

Example 7

Susan had $\frac{2}{3}$ as much money as Mary at first. After receiving $\frac{1}{2}$ of Susan's money, Mary had $210. How much money did Susan have at first?

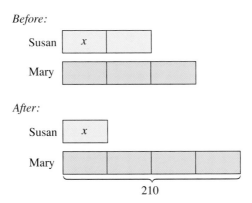

Let Susan's money be $2x$ and Mary's money be $3x$ at first. We form the equation:

$$4x = 210$$

The solution is $x = 52.5$.

Susan's money at first = $\$(2x) = \$105$

Example 8

Susan had $\frac{2}{3}$ as much money as Mary at first. After receiving $\frac{1}{2}$ of Mary's money, Susan had $210. How much money did Susan have at first?

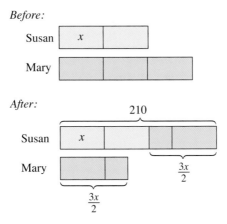

Let Susan's money be $2x$ and Mary's money be $3x$ at first. We form the equation:

$$2x + \frac{3x}{2} = 210$$

The solution is $x = 60$.

Susan's money at first = $\$(2x) = \$120$

Example 9

$\frac{3}{5}$ of the beads in a box are yellow beads. The rest are orange and blue beads. The ratio of the number of orange beads to the number of blue beads is 4 : 5. If there are 30 more blue beads than orange beads, how many yellow beads are there?

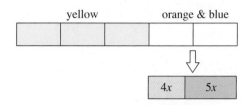

Let the number of orange beads and blue beads be $4x$ and $5x$ respectively. We form the equation:

$5x - 4x = 30$

The solution is $x = 30$.

Number of yellow beads $= 3(\frac{9x}{2}) = 405$

More examples are given as follows.

Example 10

A box contains a total of 200 blue and yellow beads. $\frac{2}{3}$ of the blue beads and $\frac{1}{2}$ of the yellow beads are taken out and used to make a necklace. If there are 30 fewer blue beads than yellow beads in the necklace, how many beads are left in the box? [90]

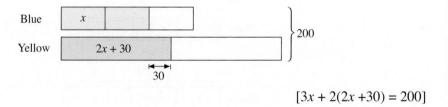

$[3x + 2(2x + 30) = 200]$

Example 11

$\frac{3}{5}$ of the students in Sec 1A and $\frac{2}{3}$ of the students in Sec 1B are girls. Both classes have the same number of girls. Sec 1A has 4 more boys than Sec 1B. How many students are there in Sec 1A? [40]

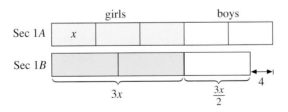

$$[2x = \frac{3x}{2} + 4]$$

Example 12

The number of fifty-cent coins and twenty-cent coins are in the ratio 2 : 3. If 4 of the fifty-cent coins are exchanged for twenty-cent coins, the ratio will become 2 : 7. What is the total value ($) of the set of coins? [$9.60]

Method 1

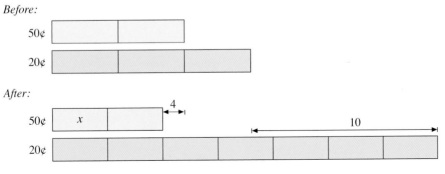

$$[\frac{2x + 4}{7x - 10} = \frac{2}{3}]$$

Method 2

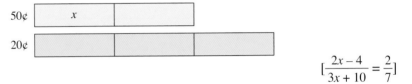

$$[\frac{2x - 4}{3x + 10} = \frac{2}{7}]$$

The Part-Whole Model for Percentage

In the part-whole model, we may express a part as a percentage of the whole. We take the whole as the base (100%), e.g.

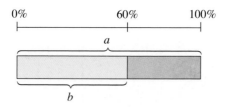

The pictorial model shows that b is 60% of a.
In this case, a comprises 100 units, and b is equal to 60 units.

We write $b = 0.6a$.

The part-whole model can be used to show the relationship between the new value of a quantity and its original value after an increase or a decrease.

Let the original value be x.

(a) The following model shows an increase of 20%.

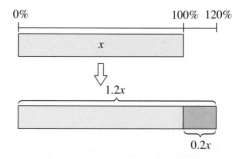

Here the increase is $0.2x$, and the new value is $1.2x$.

(b) The following model shows a decrease of 40%.

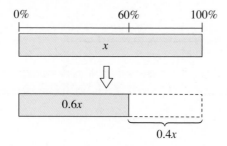

Here the decrease is $0.4x$, and the new value is $0.6x$.

The Comparison Model for Percentage

In the comparison model, we may express one quantity as a percentage of the other. For example, to compare b relative to a, we take a as the base (100%), e.g.

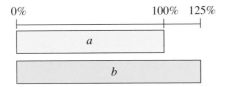

The model shows that b is 125% of a. That is, b is 25% more than a.
In this case, a comprises 100 units, and b is equal to 125 units.
We write $b = 1.25a$.

Here b is 25% more than a, but a is not 25% less than b. Indeed,

$$b = 1.25a \qquad \Rightarrow \qquad a = \frac{b}{1.25} = 0.8b$$

This shows that a is 80% of b.
That is, a is 20% less than b.

Example 13

Mrs Tan has a VIP card that entitles her to a discount of 30% off her dinner bill. If she pays $133 for her dinner, how much is the original bill?

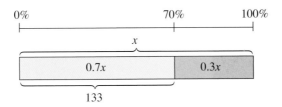

Let the original bill be x. We form the equation:

$$0.7x = 133$$

The solution is $x = 190$.

The original bill is $190.

Example 14

Jane saved 20% more in January than in February. If she saved a total of $330 in the two months, how much did she save in February?

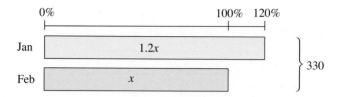

Let Jane save $x in February. We form the equation:

$$x + 1.2x = 330$$

The solution is $x = 150$.

Jane saved $150 in February.

Example 15

Mrs Tan spent $\frac{2}{3}$ of her money on a handbag. She spent 40% of the remaining money on a dress. If the handbag cost $80 more than the dress, how much money did she have at first?

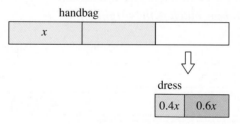

Let Mrs Tan have $3x at first. We form the equation:

$$2x - 0.4x = 80$$

The solution is $x = 50$.

Mrs Tan's money = $(3x) = $150

Example 16

A sum of money is shared among three persons A, B and C so that A receives 10% more than B, and B receives 10% more than C. If A receives $525 more than C, find the sum of money.

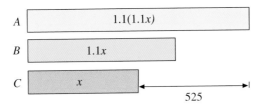

Let C receive $\$x$. We form the equation:

$$1.1(1.1x) - x = 525$$

The solution is $x = 2500$.

Sum of money = $\$(1.21x + 1.1x + x) = \$8275$

Example 17

There are twice as many boys as girls in a choir. If the number of boys is decreased by 30%, by what percentage must the number of girls be increased (or decreased) so that there will be an equal number of boys and girls in the choir?

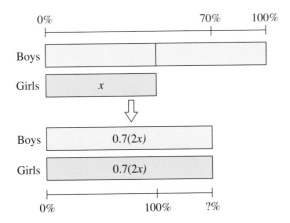

$$\text{Percentage increase} = \frac{0.7(2x) - x}{x} = 0.4 = 40\%$$

Example 18

The ratio of the number of boys to the number of girls is 5 : 6. It is given that 30% of the boys wear glasses, and there is an equal number of boys and girls who wear glasses. What percentage of the girls wear glasses?

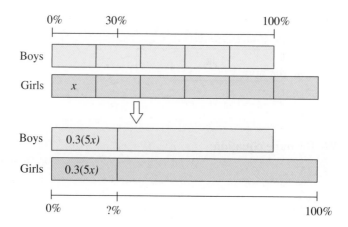

$$\text{Percentage} = \frac{0.3(5x)}{6x} = 0.25 = 25\%$$

Conclusion

Algebra is the key to the learning of higher mathematics. Nevertheless it is a worldwide concern that many students have difficulties making the transition from arithmetic to algebra, especially when they attempt to formulate algebraic equations for solving problems. The integration of the model-drawing method and the algebraic method provides an enriching opportunity for students to engage in the construction and interpretation of algebraic equations through meaningful and active learning. We hope that this approach will help more students develop their competence and confidence in using the algebraic method.

References

Beckmann, S. (2004). Solving algebra and other story problems with simple diagrams: A method demonstrated in grade 4–6 texts used in Singapore. *The Mathematics Educator, 14*(1), 42–46.

Cheong, N. P. (2002). The teaching of primary mathematics and the model approach to problem solving. *Mathematics Newsletter* (Issue No. 4). Singapore: Ministry of Education.

Fong, H. K. (1994). Bridging the gap between secondary and primary mathematics. *Teaching and Learning, 14*(2), 73–84.

Kho, T. H. (1987). Mathematical models for solving arithmetic problems. *Proceedings of the Fourth Southeast Asian Conference on Mathematics Education (ICMI-SEAMS)*, 345–351. Singapore: Institute of Education.

Ng, S. F. (2001). Secondary school students' perceptions of the relationship between the model method and algebra. *Proceedings of the Twelfth International Commission of Mathematical Instruction (ICMI) Study Conference* (pp. 468–474). Melbourne, Australia: The University of Melbourne.

Solving Challenging Algebra
Word Problems

In this article, we illustrate how the Model Method can be integrated with the algebraic method to help students solve challenging algebra word problems in secondary school mathematics. The following examples, taken from a Singapore Mathematics textbook for Secondary One[+], illustrate the approach.

Example 1

A certain amount of water is poured from a jug into an empty mug so that the amount of water in the mug is $\frac{1}{6}$ the amount of water left in the jug. If 50 ml of water is further poured from the jug to the mug, the amount of water in the mug will be $\frac{1}{5}$ of that left in the jug. Find the original amount of water in the jug.

Students may draw a pictorial model to represent the problem situation.

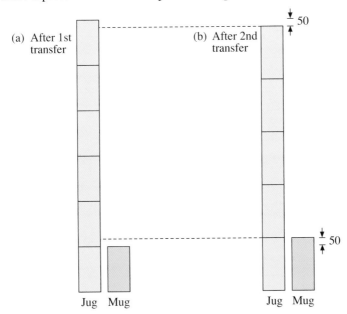

Part (a) shows the amounts of water in the two containers after the first transfer, and part (b) shows the amounts after the second transfer.

[+] *Mathematics Matters Express p. 136. Published by EPB Pan Pacific, 2007*

The model can also be presented as shown below:

After 1st transfer:

After 2nd transfer:

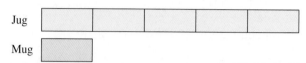

From the model, students can formulate an algebraic equation to solve the problem. Let the amount of water in the mug and the jug after the first transfer be x ml and $6x$ ml respectively.

After 1st transfer:

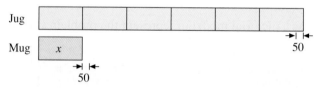

After 2nd transfer:

Jug

Mug

Variation 1

After the second transfer, the amount of water in the mug and the jug are $(x + 50)$ ml and $(6x - 50)$ ml respectively.

After 1st transfer:

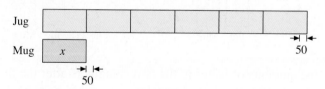

After 2nd transfer:

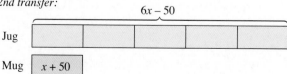

From the model, students obtain the equation:

$$6x - 50 = 5(x + 50)$$

The solution of the equation is $x = 300$.

$$7x = 2100$$

The original amount of water is 2100 ml.

Variation 2

The amount of water in the mug and the jug after the second transfer can also be expressed as $(x + 50)$ ml and $5(x + 50)$ ml respectively.

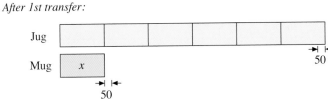

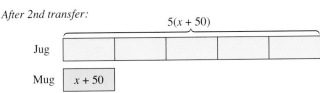

From the model, students obtain the equation:

$$6x - 5(x + 50) = 50$$

The solution of the equation is $x = 300$.

$$7x = 2100$$

The original amount of water is 2100 ml.

The following are alternative solutions to the problem when students let x ml be a different unknown quantity.

Variation 3

Let the amount of water in the mug after the second transfer be x ml.

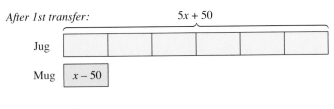

133

From the model, students obtain the equation:

$$5x + 50 = 6(x - 50)$$

The solution of the equation is $x = 350$.

$$6x = 2100$$

The original amount of water is 2100 ml.

Variation 4

Let the amount of water in the jug after the first transfer be x ml.

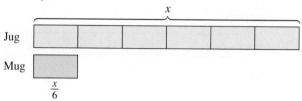

After 1st transfer:

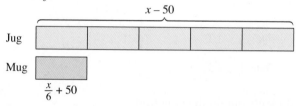

After 2nd transfer:

From the model, students obtain the following equation to solve the problem:

$$x - 50 = 5(\frac{x}{6} + 50)$$

The solution of the equation is $x = 1800$.

$$x + \frac{x}{6} = 2100$$

The original amount of water is 2100 ml.

Example 2

At a musical concert, class A tickets were sold at $4 each, class B tickets at $2 each, and souvenir programmes at $1 each. $\frac{3}{4}$ of the audience who bought class A tickets and $\frac{2}{3}$ of the audience who bought class B tickets also bought the programmes. The total amount of money collected from both types of tickets was $1400 and the amount of money collected from the programmes was $350. Find the total number of people who attended the concert.

Let x and y be the number of people who bought class A and class B tickets respectively. The problem can be solved by formulating a pair of simultaneous linear equations:

$$4x + 2y = 1400$$
$$\frac{3}{4}x + \frac{2}{3}y = 350$$

The solution to the pair of equations is $x = 200$ and $y = 300$.

$$x + y = 500$$

The total number of people is 500.

The problem can also be solved by a pictorial method as follows:

Let $4x$ and $3y$ be the number of people who bought class A and class B tickets respectively. Students can draw a pictorial model to represent the problem situation as follows:

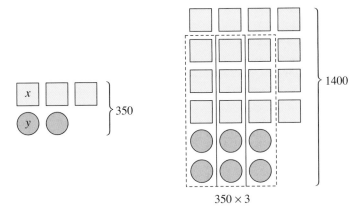

350×3

By eliminating 3 groups of 350 from 1400 as shown, students find the value of x as follows:

$$7x = 1400 - 350 \times 3$$
$$= 350 \qquad \longrightarrow \quad x = 50$$

By eliminating $3x$ from 350, students find the value of y as follows:

$$2y = 350 - 50 \times 3$$
$$= 200 \qquad \longrightarrow \quad y = 100$$

Total number of people $= 4x + 3y = 500$

The problem is regarded as a challenging problem before students learn simultaneous linear equations. They may solve the problem by formulating a linear equation from the following model:

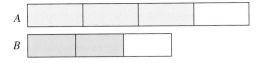

The model shows that $\frac{3}{4}$ of A and $\frac{2}{3}$ of B bought the programmes.

Variation 1

Let 1 unit in *B* be *x*. Then the total number of people who bought the programmes in *B* is 2*x*, and that in *A* is 350 − 2*x*.

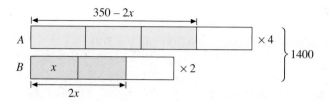

From the model, students obtain the following equation to solve the problem:

$$4(\frac{4}{3})(350 - 2x) + 2(3x) = 1400$$

The solution of the equation is $x = 100$.

$$\frac{4}{3}(350 - 2x) + 3x = 500$$

The total number of people is 500.

Variation 2

Let 1 unit in *A* be *x* . Then the total number of people who bought the programmes in *A* is 3*x* , and that in *B* is 350 − 3*x*.

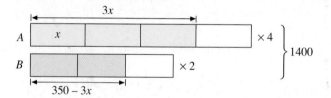

From the model, students obtain the following equation to solve the problem:

$$4(4x) + 2(\frac{3}{2}) (350 - 3x) = 1400$$

The solution of the equation is $x = 50$.

$$4x + \frac{3}{2} (350 - 3x) = 500$$

The total number of people is 500.